Properties of Solids and their Atomic Structures

Properties of Solids and their Atomic Structures

H. J. M. Bowen

Lecturer in Chemistry
University of Reading

McGRAW-HILL Publishing Company Limited
LONDON · New York · Toronto · Sydney

Published by
McGRAW-HILL Publishing Company Limited
MAIDENHEAD · BERKSHIRE · ENGLAND

94056

PRINTED AND BOUND IN GREAT BRITAIN

Contents

Preface

This book has been written from the notes of a course of lectures given to second-year chemistry students at Reading University. It is intended as an introduction to the subject of solids, and should be understandable by chemists with a rudimentary grasp of quantum theory and thermodynamics. While a number of excellent advanced texts have been written on the subject of solids, most of these are concerned with detailed mathematical models of the different types of solid. In this brief study, mathematics has been excluded deliberately in order to emphasize the physical concepts involved, and the relation between macroscopic properties and the arrangement of atoms in solids is treated in a qualitative manner.

A second major omission concerns the experimental methods used to provide the enormous amount of experimental data from which our ideas on the solid state are derived. Once again, this omission has been made good by several recent texts to which readers are referred on pages 118–122.

It is my impression that many students use physical and chemical terms which they are unable to define. A feature of this book is the extensive glossary which attempts to define most of the terms used with respect to such indefinable quantities as mass, length, time, energy, and electric charge. Units have presented a problem since, for example, chemists use both the kilocalorie and the electron volt as units of energy. An energy interconversion table has, therefore, been included at the end of the book.

Almost all the figures have been drawn or redrawn specially for this book and, while many are original, my thanks are due to the many authors from whose works the others were taken and to whom acknowledgement is made on the appropriate pages. I would especially like to thank R. M. Barrer for permission to copy Figs. 2.13 and 2.14, and W. T. Read for permission to copy Figs. 6.9 and 6.10. Finally, I am most grateful to Dr C. D. Clark, who has read the entire text and corrected many errors.

H. J. M. Bowen

1. Introduction to solids

A solid is a material whose shape and volume do not change with time if the temperature remains constant. Thus it contrasts with a liquid, which has a fixed volume but no definite shape, or a gas, which has neither its volume nor its shape fixed by temperature. On a submicroscopic scale, a solid can be defined as an array of atoms, molecules, or ions whose mean positions do not change with time. Some scientists prefer to restrict the term solids to arrays which possess some degree of order and symmetry, and exclude such materials as glass, which is then classified as a supercooled liquid. Our definition agrees with the average man's conception that glass is a solid.

However we define a solid, there is an important distinction to be drawn between crystalline and amorphous solids. *Crystalline* solids contain ordered arrays of atoms and hence possess symmetry (see appendix, page 114). This book deals almost exclusively with crystalline solids. Solids which are not crystalline are said to be *amorphous*. Amorphous solids can be experimentally distinguished from crystalline solids by at least three independent criteria. Firstly, they melt over a range of temperature which is usually several degrees in magnitude, whereas crystalline solids have sharp melting points which can be measured to $\pm 0.01°$ or better. Secondly, amorphous solids give a diffuse pattern when they diffract X-rays, the main feature of which is a series of concentric rings. This pattern is quite different from the sharp, symmetrical pattern of discrete spots which is obtained when X-rays are diffracted by a crystalline solid (Figs. 1.1 and 1.2). Thirdly, all crystalline solids are more or less *anisotropic*, that is, some of their properties depend on the direction in which they are

1

measured with respect to the axes of the crystal. Amorphous solids are all isotropic.

Amorphous solids are not common, though they include many familiar materials. Plastic sulphur is amorphous, while beryllium fluoride and the oxides of boron, silicon, and germanium all have

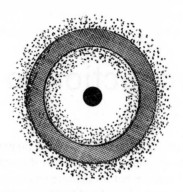

Fig. 1.1. X-ray diffraction pattern from amorphous silica.

*Fig. 1.2. X-ray diffraction pattern from crystalline diamond, [100]
direction, showing four-fold symmetry, slightly distorted due to
cylindrical nature of camera.*

amorphous and crystalline forms. All types of glass are amorphous, as is shown by their behaviour on melting, and so are many silicates, borates, and phosphates of potassium and other metals. Amorphous organic solids include most higher alkanes, which form glasses when rapidly cooled, synthetic polymers such as polyethylene and polyvinyl chloride, and some naturally occurring materials such as pitch and beeswax.

Classification of solid properties

The properties of solids are so numerous that it is possible to classify them in several ways, which are not mutually exclusive. Only *intensive* properties, which are independent of the volume of the sample, are included here. Intensive properties may be classified as follows:

1. Properties depending on order.
2. Properties depending on binding energy.
3. Properties depending on energy transitions of the constituent particles.
4. Properties depending on structural defects.
5. Properties depending on surface configurations.

Properties depending on order are not found in amorphous solids, nor in liquids apart from smectic and nematic liquids. They include sharply defined melting points, and the ability to give symmetrical patterns of discrete spots by diffracting X-rays, neutrons, or electrons of suitable energies, as mentioned above. The existence of polymorphic forms of many solids, and the sharpness of the transition temperatures between these forms, are also characteristic of order. Cleavage, and some forms of plastic deformation, depend on crystalline order, as do the rare phenomena of ferromagnetism, ferrimagnetism, antiferromagnetism, ferroelectricity, antiferroelectricity, pyroelectricity, and piezoelectricity, which are discussed below. All these properties are completely destroyed by melting or dissolution.

Note that optically active crystals have no rotation-inversion axes, and lack a centre of symmetry. If this is due to the presence of asymmetric molecules, such as CHFClBr, the optical activity is not lost on melting. Many crystals, such as Te, HgS, and SiO_2 (quartz), lack a centre of symmetry owing to the arrangement of atoms in their unit cells. These materials lose their optical activity on melting or dissolution.

Properties depending chiefly on binding energy include hardness, compressibility, ease of dissolution, thermal expansion and the melting points and transition temperatures. Some of these properties have analogues in the liquid state, where the average binding energy is usually of the same order of magnitude as it is in the solid.

Properties depending on energy transitions include most of the interactions of solids with electromagnetic radiation, other than optical activity, e.g., absorption spectra over the whole range from X-rays to radio waves, and hence colour, transparency, and opacity in various regions of the spectrum. They also include properties which depend to a large extent on the vibrations of the lattice of atoms forming the solid, such as specific heat and thermal conductivity. Diamagnetism and paramagnetism are properties of the electrons in a solid, just as nuclear magnetism and radioactivity, if any, are properties of the nuclei. Metals, and to a less marked extent semiconductors, have several unusual properties as a result of the unlocalized electrons in them. These properties include reflectivity, exceptional thermal and electrical conductivity, and the power of emitting electrons on heating or bombarding with energetic radiation. All these properties change relatively little on melting, and some of them persist in the gas phase.

Properties depending markedly on structural defects have mostly been mentioned under the other headings. They include unusual or forbidden spectral lines, abnormal colours and luminescence, some forms of plastic deformation, and the electrical conductivity of semiconductors and ionic solids. Apart from the last-named, these are characteristic solid properties which are lost on melting.

Properties depending on surface configurations include friction, surface conductivity, adsorption, and heterogeneous catalysis. These again are characteristic of solids, but are often irreproducible and dependent on the history of the specimen used.

Classification of crystalline solids

Five types of crystalline solid are recognized here, namely: molecular, covalent, ionic, metallic, and semiconducting solids. Each of these has a distinct type of bonding in the solid state, which gives rise to distinctive macroscopic properties. Although there are intermediates between these types, most real solids can be classified as predominantly one or other type, and fifty-fifty intermediates are rare.

Molecular solids (e.g., argon, iodine (Fig. 1.3), organic compounds) are made up of discrete molecules, or rarely atoms, separated from all other molecules by regions of negligible electron density. The molecules may sometimes be weakly bonded together by hydrogen bonds (e.g., ice) or pi-bonds (e.g., anthracene), but they are never linked by true chemical bonds.

Covalent solids (e.g., diamond, Fig. 1.4) are those in which the constituent atoms are linked by a continuous framework of covalent bonds, so that each crystal either contains large, polymeric molecules or is itself a single giant molecule. The framework may be one-dimensional (e.g., selenium), two-dimensional (e.g., red phosphorus, graphite), or three-dimensional (e.g., diamond).

Ionic solids (e.g., potassium fluoride, Fig. 1.5) contain discrete, electrically charged ions, separated by regions of negligible electron

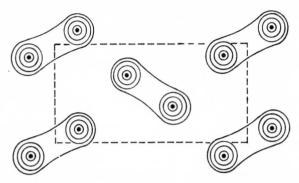

Fig. 1.3. Diagrammatic electron density map of solid I_2. The top of the unit cell, viewed from above, is outlined.

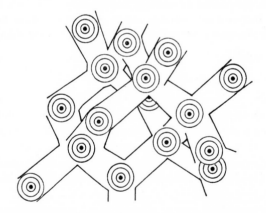

Fig. 1.4. Diagrammatic electron density map of diamond (for unit cell of diamond see Fig. 1.12).

density from the oppositely charged ions. The ions are held in place by electrostatic forces, and may be simple (monatomic), complex (polyatomic), or one ion may be polymeric in one, two, or three dimensions.

Metallic solids (e.g., aluminium, Fig. 1.6) consist of an ordered array of cations held together by a fluid pool of valency electrons which

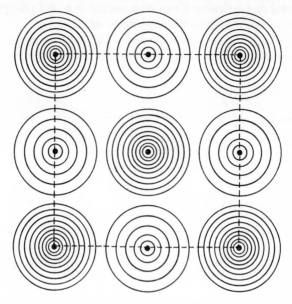

Fig. 1.5. Diagrammatic electron density map of potassium fluoride; only the upper plane of the unit cell is shown (cf. Fig. 4.1).

Fig. 1.6. Diagrammatic electron density map of a single layer of atoms in solid aluminium.

they share. The cations are always simple, but there is no reason why complex cations such as ammonium should not form metallic solids under suitable conditions, as at very high pressures.

Semiconducting solids (e.g., germanium, lead sulphide) are covalent, often with some ionic character, or rarely molecular solids in which a small percentage of the valency electrons are able to move freely within the crystal and profoundly modify the macroscopic properties.

In order to classify a solid into one of these types, we need to know its appearance, melting point, and how its electrical conductivity varies with temperature T. The following simple key is useful, though by no means infallible; for example, it would classify graphite as a metal, which it is not.

Insulator at all temperatures: melting point $< 600°$K *Molecular*
                       melting point $> 600°$K *Covalent*

Insulator at low T, conductivity increases exponentially with T:
                       transparent   *Ionic*
                       opaque   *Semiconducting*

Good conductor, conductivity decreases with T: *Metallic*

An outline of some important properties for the five types of solids recognized here is given in Table 1.1.

Isomorphism

The geometrical arrangement of atoms in solids can be obtained from measurements of the diffraction of X-rays or neutrons (Wells, 1962; Bacon, 1962). If two solids contain a similar arrangement of geometrically similar structural units, they are said to be *isomorphous*. Examples of isomorphous solids are: Ar and Ne (molecular), Graphite and BN (two-dimensional covalent), NaCl and KCl (ionic), Zr and Hf (metallic), and Si and Ge (semiconducting).

Similarity in chemical formulae and behaviour does not necessarily imply isomorphism; thus KCl is not isomorphic with CsCl at NTP. Conversely, isomorphism does not require similarity in chemical formulae, as is shown by the isomorphic set $K_2TiF_6 . H_2O$, $K_2NbOF_5 . H_2O$, and $K_2WO_2F_4 . H_2O$. In the same way the fact that two solids form mixed crystals does not imply that they are isomorphic (e.g., CaF_2 forms mixed crystals with YF_3), nor does isomorphism require that mixed crystals can be made (e.g., $CaCO_3$ and $NaNO_3$).

Table 1.1

Classification of solids

Property	Molecular solids	Covalent solids	Ionic solids	Metals	Semiconductors
Binding energy (kcal mole^{-1})	2–10	100–300	150–320	30–200	100–300
Melting point (degrees K)	< 600	500–3700	700–3300	230–4150	1200–2500
Hardness	soft	soft/hard	hard	malleable/hard	hard
Compressibility	moderate	moderate/small	small	small	small
Ultra-violet spectra	absorb	absorb, peaks broad	absorb, peaks sharp	transparent, in part	absorb
Visible spectra	may absorb	transparent	transparent, may absorb	reflect, rarely also absorb	mostly opaque
Infra-red spectra	absorb if polar	absorb if polar	absorb strongly	reflect	absorb if polar
Thermal conductivity (cal sec^{-1}cm^{-1}deg^{-1})	10^{-4}–10^{-2}	0·01–1·5	0·005–0·05	0·1–1	0·01–0·2

2

	$10^{14}–10^{22}$ (except anthracene)	$10^{14}–10^{22}$ (except graphite)	$10^9–10^{19}$ (except AgI)	$10^{-5}–10^{-3}$	$10^2–10^9$
Electrical resistivity R (ohm cm):					
Effect of rise in T		negligible	decreases R	increases R	decreases R
Electron emission	rare	none	rare	thermal and photoelectric	thermal and photoelectric
Ferromagnetism	none	none	rare ferrimagnets	rare	rare ferrimagnets
Ferroelectricity	none	none	rare	none	rare
Optical activity	frequent, kept on dissolution	rare, lost on dissolution	rare, kept on dissolution	none	none
Liquid solvents	dissolve in like solvents	insoluble; dissolve with destruction of lattice	dissolve in a few polar solvents and molten salts	dissolve in metals with atoms of similar size	dissolve only with lattice destruction
Examples	He–Xe, H_2, N_2, O_2, P_4, S_8, $F_2–I_2$, most organic compounds	Diamond, graphite, Se (grey)	NaCl, CsCl, CaF_2, TiO_2, most metallic fluorides and oxides	Al, Ca, Fe, Hg, Na, W, etc., alloys + hydrides, borides carbides and nitrides of Groups III–VIB	Si, Ge, SiC, GaAs, PbS

Classic examples of variations in structure in substances with similar formulae include $CaCO_3$, $CaSiO_3$, and $CaTiO_3$. These are all ionic solids, but while CO_3^{--} forms a well-known anion, calcium silicate contains cyclic $Si_3O_9^{6-}$ anions and calcium titanate consists of Ca^{++}, Ti^{4+}, and O^{--} units. Another example is the set of oxides SO_3, CrO_3, MoO_3, WO_3, and UO_3. These have the following structures:

SO_3: This has two forms, one made up of molecular, S_3O_9 ring polymers, and the other made up of one-dimensional covalent S_nO_{3n} chain polymers.

CrO_3: This is a one-dimensional covalent structure containing Cr_nO_{3n} molecules.

MoO_3: This is a two-dimensional covalent structure containing infinite layers.

WO_3: This is an essentially ionic oxide with a slightly distorted edge-centred cubic structure.

UO_3: This is a more complex ionic structure in which linear complex UO_2^{++} ions can be distinguished. When deficient in oxygen, it is a semiconductor.

Polymorphism

A solid is said to be *polymorphic* if it exists in more than one form. Another name for polymorphism, sometimes restricted to the elements, is *allotropy*. Polymorphism is almost restricted to solids, though it is also found in a few liquids containing long molecules, and in liquid helium-4. Apart from differences in appearance and other properties, polymorphs usually differ in their X-ray and/or neutron diffraction patterns. There are two kinds of polymorphism, which are readily distinguished by the properties which change discontinuously at the transition point. All transition points are experimentally accessible, though not readily so in such cases as graphite and diamond (Fig. 1.7). Rhombic and monoclinic sulphur are examples of polymorphic forms in which the transition is said to be *sharp* or *first order*. On heating the low temperature, alpha, or rhombic form, there is a sharp transition to the monoclinic or beta form at 112·8°C, which takes place over a range of temperature less than 0·001°C in extent; this transition is reversed on cooling. As shown in Fig. 1.8, the density of the two forms differs considerably and there is a discontinuous change in density at the transition point, just as there is at the melting point. General characteristics of all sharp transitions are:

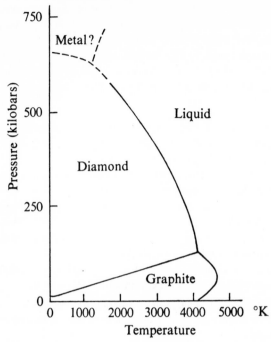

Fig. 1.7. Phase diagram for carbon (after Bundy, 1963).

1. The transition temperature is sharply defined.
2. The density, and also the entropy and heat content per gram of the sample, change discontinuously at the transition point.
3. The Clapeyron equation is obeyed, i.e.

$$\Delta S / \Delta V = \mathrm{d}p / \mathrm{d}T$$

where ΔS and ΔV are the entropy and volume changes in the transition and $\mathrm{d}p/\mathrm{d}T$ is the rate of change of pressure with absolute temperature.

Melting is a typical sharp transition.

In *gradual transitions* the transition temperature is not so sharply defined, and the transition takes place over a range of temperature which is usually less than $0 \cdot 01°C$ but may be as much as $100°C$. Discontinuous changes in density, entropy, and heat content are not found, but instead the specific heat at constant pressure $C_p (= T \partial S / \partial T)$, the compressibility $(= -V^{-1} \partial V / \partial p)$ and the coefficient of thermal expansion $(= V^{-1} \partial V / \partial T)$ show maxima at the transition point. The

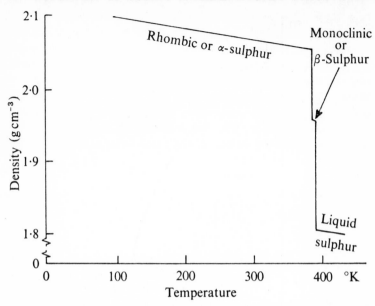

Fig. 1.8. *Density of sulphur as a function of temperature, showing discontinuous changes at the transition point and the melting point.*

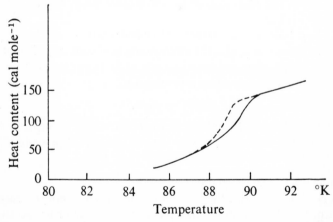

Fig. 1.9. *Heat content of solid HBr near its transition temperature (after Eucken, 1939), showing hysteresis: ——— heating; - - - - cooling.*

Clapeyron relation is not obeyed, and the transitions involve irreversible absorption of energy and show hysteresis (Fig. 1.9).

In addition, the low temperature form may possess one or more new properties not found in the high temperature form, such as double refraction, ferromagnetism, ferroelectricity, piezoelectricity or super-conduction. Two kinds of maxima in the specific heat/temperature curve serve to distinguish two subclasses of gradual transitions. When C_p increases rapidly during the transition and then falls discontinuously at its completion, the transition is said to be a *lambda-type* transition, e.g., the transition in KH_2PO_4 at 120°K (Fig. 1.10). When the maximum in C_p is less sharp and more nearly

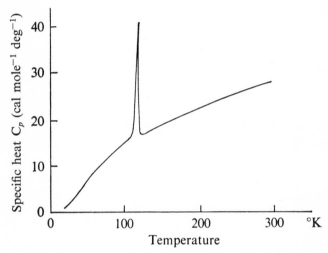

Fig. 1.10. Variation of specific heat of KH_2PO_4 with temperature, showing a λ-point at 120°K (after Stephenson and Hooley, 1944).

symmetrical, with a tail on the high temperature side, the transition is said to be a *Schottky-type* transition. Both types of gradual transition are found in ferric ammonium sulphate at very low temperatures (Fig. 1.11).

The various types of polymorphism can be interpreted in atomic terms as follows. Sharp transitions involve a change in the packing of either atoms (e.g., calcium metal, which changes from cubic close-packed to hexagonal close-packed at 713°K), ions (e.g., caesium chloride, which changes from a CsCl to a NaCl structure at 718°K) or molecules (e.g., the S_8 ring polymers found in both rhombic and monoclinic sulphur, which are packed more loosely in the mono-clinic form). In a few cases the difference in packing may be profound, as for example in carbon or phosphorus. The structures of diamond and graphite are shown in Fig. 1.12, and those of white and black phosphorus in Fig. 1.13 (the structure of red phosphorus is still unknown). These exceptional cases are notable for the experimental inaccessibility of their transition points. The difference in packing explains the different densities of the two forms, while the change in order accounts for their different entropies, and the change in binding energy is responsible for their different heat contents.

Gradual transitions involve a number of unrelated properties, but most of them are now understood in a qualitative fashion. Lambda-type

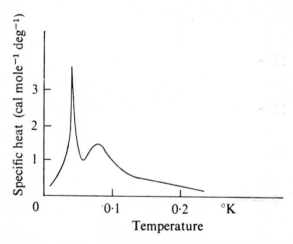

Fig. 1.11. Variation of specific heat with temperature below 0·2°K for ferric ammonium sulphate, showing a λ-transition at 0·04°K and a Schottky transition at 0·08°K (after Cooke and Kurti, 1949).

transitions are thought to arise by co-operative interactions between ordered atoms as they attain the disordered state. The probability of any atom becoming disordered in an ordered lattice is not purely random in this type of change, but depends on the number of neighbouring atoms which have become disordered as a result of thermal motion. Hence this type of change begins slowly and ends very rapidly as the temperature is raised. Examples of order–disorder transitions are found in many molecular solids, as well as in those containing finite complex ions. For example, solid methane undergoes a transition at 5°K, and ammonium chloride a transition at 243°K, below which temperatures the CH_4 molecules and NH_4^+ ions respectively are believed to be completely ordered. Above the transition points these species occur in two or more orientations in the unit cell, in a disordered manner. The number of equivalent orientations in the disordered state can be estimated from the entropy change ΔS per

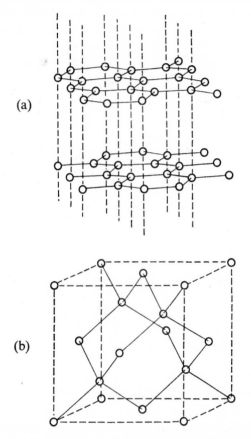

(a)

(b)

Fig. 1.12. Crystal structures of (a) graphite and (b) diamond (after Wells, 1962). Full lines represent covalent bonds. In (a) dotted lines show linear rows of atoms, in (b) dotted lines outline the unit crystal cell.

mole during the transition, since it is given by $e^{\Delta S/kN}$, where k is Boltzmann's constant and N is Avogadro's number. Order–disorder transitions giving rise to lambda-type anomalies are also found in many metallic alloys. For example in brass, CuZn, the copper and zinc atoms are arranged alternately in the lattice at low temperatures and randomly at high temperatures (Fig. 1.14); this transition starts at about 370°K and terminates at 740°K. In ferromagnetic, ferrimagnetic, and antiferromagnetic solids the order is confined to the spins or magnetic moments of certain unpaired electrons. As the temperature is raised the abnormal magnetic susceptibility is lost and

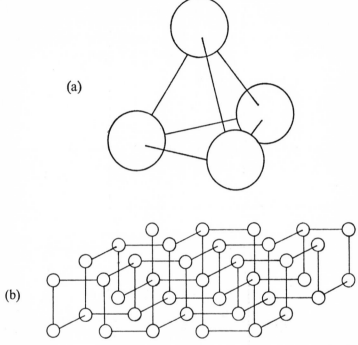

Fig. 1.13. Crystal structures of (a) white phosphorus, and (b) black phosphorus (after Wells, 1962): full lines represent covalent bonds.

replaced by paramagnetism, usually by way of a lambda-type transition. Ferroelectric and superconducting solids also lose their special properties by lambda-type transitions as the temperature is raised.

Schottky transitions arise when atoms or molecules possess energy levels which are independent of the energy levels of the solid lattice. At low temperatures the atoms all exist in their lowest possible energy states, but on raising the temperature they attain higher energy states at random, with no co-operative effect from neighbouring atoms. Schottky transitions are rare, but are found at very low temperatures, as when paramagnetic ions lose the energy they acquire from the magnetic field of the crystal in which they are sited, or when magnetic nuclei change from an upper energy level to the ground state. Nickel sulphate hexahydrate and ferric ammonium sulphate (Fig. 1.11) undergo transitions of this type below 10°K.

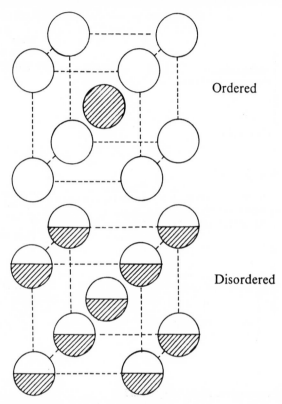

Ordered

Disordered

Fig. 1.14. Ordered and disordered arrays of atoms in β-brass, CuZn: ○ = Cu, ⊘ = Zn, ⊘ = Cu or Zn. The transition temperature between the two forms is about 740°K.

Effects of temperature on solids

When considering the effects of temperature on solids, it helps if the variation of properties is plotted against $\log T$ rather than against T itself (Fig. 1.15). This presentation both emphasizes the unattainability of absolute zero, and justifies the current efforts of physicists towards the study of temperatures below 1°K. Since room temperature is about 300°K, or about the middle of the range spanned in

Fig. 1.15, it makes a logical starting point for looking at this figure in more detail.

If the temperature is raised one order of magnitude to 3000°K, nearly all solids become molten or vaporized, though a few elements, borides, carbides, nitrides, and oxides still remain solid (Table 1.2).

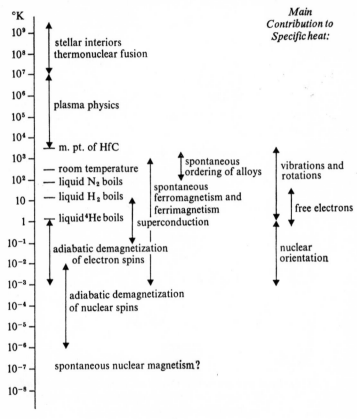

Fig. 1.15. Logarithmic temperature plot.

The most refractory solids known are hafnium carbide and tantalum carbide, both of which melt at just over 4150°K.

Since temperature is a measure of the mean kinetic energy of atoms, and the mean energy of an atom at temperature T is $3kT/2$ where k is Boltzmann's constant, the main effect of raising the temperature of a solid is to increase the thermal motion of the atoms or molecules

Table 1.2

Melting points or subliming points of some involatile solids ($^\circ K$)

Substance	m.p.	Substance	m.p.	Substance	m.p.
Elements:		Carbides:		Nitrides:	
C(diamond)	3773	HfC	4160	BN	3270(subl.)
C(graphite)	3925(subl.)	NbC	3773	HfN	3578
Os	2973	SiC	2970(subl.)	TaN	3633
Re	3440	TaC	4153	TiN	3203
W	3683	TiC	3413	ZrN	3253
Ta	3269	VC	3083		
		WC	3143	Oxides:	
Borides:		W_2C	3133	HfO_2	3085
HfB_2	3270	ZrC	3813	MgO	3073
NbB_2	3170			ZrO_2	2973
TaB_2	3270				
TiB_2	3170				
WB_2	3170				
ZrB_2	3270				

present. As the solid is heated, the lattice and/or molecular vibrations become so vigorous that ultimately one of three things happens:

1. The lattice breaks up to form a liquid by a sharp transition, i.e., the solid melts, gaining entropy and absorbing latent heat. Example: gallium.

2. The lattice breaks up to form a gas by a sharp transition, i.e., the solid sublimes, gaining entropy and absorbing latent heat. Example: iodine.

3. The individual molecules or complex ions in the lattice, if present, break up to form other products, usually including some gases; heat may be emitted or absorbed. Example: calcium carbonate decomposing to lime and carbon dioxide.

If on the other hand the temperature is lowered from 300°K, it can be seen from Fig. 1.15 that in theory there are an infinite number of orders of magnitude of temperature available for study. In practice, temperatures below 3°K are difficult to attain, but 10^{-6}°K has been achieved. Apart from helium, all substances become solid below 3°K, and nearly all below 30°K. The key to understanding solid properties at very low temperatures is the third law of thermodynamics. This states that pure solid substances attain perfect order at absolute zero or more formally

$$\text{Limit}_{T \to 0} S = 0$$

where S is the entropy. As a consequence of the third law, several properties of pure substances such as specific heat and the coefficient of thermal expansion must also tend to zero as absolute zero is approached. Note that there is nothing in the third law which prevents the attainment of perfect order at temperatures above absolute zero. In some cases, for example superconductors and ferromagnetic materials, it is now thought that perfect order is in fact so attained, at least for small crystals.

The following effects are characteristically observed in solids on lowering the temperature:

1. Order increases (that is, entropy decreases). Atoms tend to form close-packed structures by sharp transitions. Disordered alloys become ordered by gradual transitions. Paramagnetic substances become either ferromagnetic or antiferromagnetic as the electron spins become ordered. At very low temperatures nuclear magnetism becomes ordered.

2. Vibration of atoms decreases, ultimately leaving atoms with their zero-point energy. Therefore, infra-red spectral lines vanish, and the specific heats decrease. At lower temperatures oscillation or rotation of molecules and complex ions stops, involving a gradual transition; hence the corresponding spectral lines in the microwave region disappear.

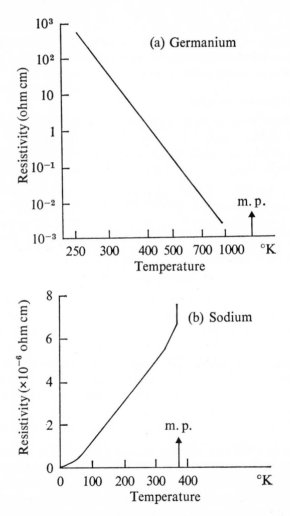

Fig. 1.16. Resistivity as a function of temperature for a semiconductor (a) germanium, and a metal (b) sodium. Note log/log scale in (a). Sodium is not known to be a superconductor.

3. The electrical conductivity of ionic solids and semiconductors tends to zero, so that these substances become insulators. On the other hand the electrical conductivity of metals increases, and many metals become perfect conductors between 0·1 and 20°K, after a gradual transition (Fig. 1.16).

4. The elastic constants of solids increase to a small extent. On the other hand the actual strengths of many solids increase dramatically, though some also become more brittle. The strengths of these solids is thought to be determined mainly by lattice defects rather than by the elastic constants measured for perfect or nearly perfect crystals.

Effects of pressure on solids

The properties of solids are usually studied at atmospheric pressure, which is approximately 1 bar, where 1 bar $= 10^6$ dynes cm^{-2}. The majority of solids are scarcely affected by reducing the pressure below atmospheric, though volatile solids such as iodine may sublime away.

Table 1.3

Pressure in kilobars required to convert some elements from insulators to metallic solids. $p_{obs.}$ was obtained from measurements of electrical resistance, and $p_{calc.}$ by extrapolation of spectral data.

Element	$p_{obs.}$	$p_{calc.}$
As_n (grey)		160
H_2		750
I_2	235	240
P_4 (white)		30
P_n (red)	40	90
S_8		400
Se_n	128	130
Te_n	40	

The study of the effects of high pressures is limited by experimental difficulties. Thus above 30 kbars it is impossible to apply hydrostatic pressure, since all known liquids have turned into solids. However, by using massive apparatus made of very strong materials such as tungsten carbide, it has proved possible to sustain a pressure of 400 kbars, and transient pressures in shock tubes may exceed this value. It is worth recalling that the pressure at the centre of the earth is probably several megabars, and that 90 per cent of the earth's interior is subject to a stress exceeding 100 kbars.

The following effects have been observed in solids on raising the pressure. They should be compared with the corresponding list of changes on lowering the temperature.

1. Order increases. Structures tend to become close-packed by sharp transitions. Hence non-conducting elements ultimately become metallic, as shown in Table 1.3.

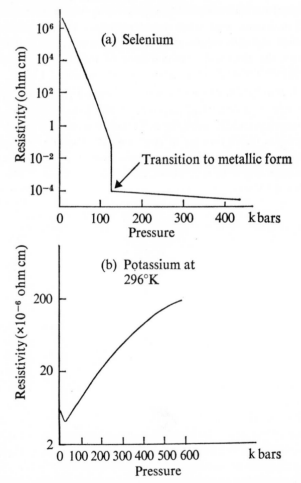

Fig. 1.17. Resistivity of a non-metal (a) selenium and a metal (b) potassium as a function of pressure (after Drickamer, 1965): the absolute resistivity scales are somewhat uncertain.

2. Vibration of atoms, and rotation of molecules and complex ions, decrease, leading to fewer or less intense spectral lines in general. On the other hand, the electronic structures of some molecules, such as H_2, N_2, O_2, and CO_2, become distorted, so that their normal spectra are augmented by new, previously forbidden, spectral lines. The thermal conductivities of most solids increase, except for some metals.

3. The electrical conductivities of ionic solids and semiconductors are not markedly affected by pressure. The electrical conductivities of molecular and some covalent solids increase and finally attain metallic values after a sharp transition. On the other hand the electrical conductivities of metals usually decrease somewhat, though in an irregular fashion (Fig. 1.17).

4. A few metals undergo sharp transitions which do not involve a change in geometrical packing. In the case of cerium, which changes markedly in density at 7 kbars, it is believed that pressure squeezes the outermost 4f electrons into the more compact 5d shell. Unexplained density changes have also been reported for Ba at 60 kbars, Bi at 25 kbars, Cd at 3 kbars, Cs at 45 kbars, and Sb at 85 kbars.

2. Molecular solids

Molecular solids consist of atoms or finite covalently bound molecules held together by forces weaker than those associated with chemical bonds. A useful measure of these forces is the *binding energy per mole*, which is the energy needed to vaporize one mole of solid; it can be measured directly for solids which sublime without decomposition, such as iodine. The lattice energy of molecular solids is usually of the order of 0.04–0.4 eV per molecule, or 1–10 kcals mole^{-1}, which is about a tenth of the binding energy of most other solids. The thermal energy of a mole of atoms at room temperature is 0.9 kcals, so the small binding energy accounts for the low melting point and small latent heat of fusion of molecular solids. Few molecular solids have a melting point exceeding $600°$K and one, namely helium, cannot be made by cooling at atmospheric pressure and will only form when exposed to a pressure of 20 bars around $1°$K. The small binding energy also accounts for the softness, poor mechanical strength, and unusually high compressibility of most molecular solids.

The way in which the molecules are packed in molecular crystals depends partly on their shapes and partly on the positions of any electrical dipoles in them. In the simplest case of spherical or nearly spherical molecules with small or zero dipole moments, the lattice is usually either cubic close-packed (Fig. 2.1) or hexagonal close-packed (Fig. 2.2). Examples of the former type of lattice include solid Ar, HCl, HBr, NH_3, and CH_4, while examples of the second type include solid H_2, N_2, and O_2 or at least their high temperature forms.

The difference between cubic and hexagonal close-packing is best demonstrated by using models. The only way that spheres can be close-packed in two-dimensional layers is shown in Fig. 1.6, where each sphere is surrounded by six other spheres. If layers of this kind are stacked one on top of another, the resulting array contains spheres close-packed in three dimensions. If the lowest layer is called A, the next or B-layer can only fit on in one way, with the centre of each B-sphere vertically above a gap in the A-layer. The third layer can either

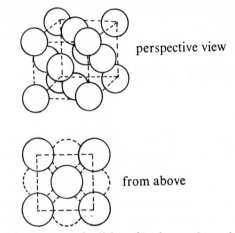

perspective view

from above

Fig. 2.1. Unit crystal cell for cubic close-packing of spheres.

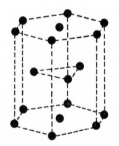

Fig. 2.2. Diagram showing hexagonal close-packing of spheres.

be a repeat of the A-layer, or rest in an alternative position with each C-sphere vertically above the contiguous gaps in both A- and B-layers. In the latter case the result is cubic close-packing, in which the layers are stacked ABCABC.... Hexagonal close-packed spheres have the layers stacked ABABAB.... These simple types of packing may be modified for non-spherical molecules, and especially where the molecules are strongly polar or contain aromatic ring systems.

In order to understand why this is so, the nature of the forces holding uncharged atoms and molecules together in the solid state must be considered. Ideally, the binding energies of related solids should be compared but, as these are not always available, the melting point is often used as a rough measure of the binding energy.

Five types of weak intermolecular forces, known collectively as Van der Waals forces, will be recognized here and considered in turn: *London forces*, *Dipole interactions*, *Hydrogen-bonding*, *Fluorine-bonding*, and *Electron overlap*.

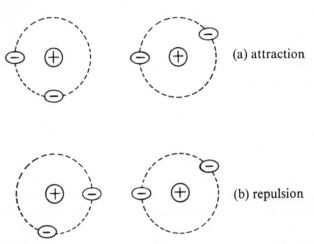

Fig. 2.3. Diagrammatic representation of London forces between two isolated helium atoms: ⊕ = He nucleus, ⊖ = electron, ––– = mean electron orbit.

London forces

London forces are the weak electrostatic forces which exist between non-polar atoms and molecules as a result of attractions between temporarily non-zero dipoles; the physical picture of this type of attraction between two helium atoms is illustrated in Fig. 2.3. Theory shows that for two molecules A and B, distance r apart, the potential energy of attraction is proportional to $\alpha_A \alpha_B r^{-6}$, where α is the *polarizability* of the molecule. The polarizability is equal to the dipole moment induced by a unit electric field. It depends very much on molecular weight, being greatest for heavy atoms and molecules. The dependence of melting point on molecular weight is illustrated by the data in Table 2.1.

Table 2.1

Melting points and molecular weights of solids containing non-polar atoms and molecules

Solid	mol. wt.	m.p.°K	Solid	mol. wt.	m.p.°K
He	4	1 ($p = 20$ bar)	H_2	2	14
Ne	20	24	F_2	38	51
Ar	40	84	Cl_2	71	171
Kr	84	104	Br_2	160	266
Xe	131	133	I_2	257	387

London forces are thought to exist in all types of solids, but in only a few solids, such as the inert gases, the halogens, hydrogen, oxygen, and nitrogen do they constitute the sole form of intermolecular attraction.

Dipole interactions

Dipole interactions are electrostatic interactions which occur not only between molecules which have dipole moments, but also between individual chemical bonds which are dipoles. Since any covalent bond between two different atoms possesses a dipole moment, that is, the electrons are shared unequally, there are many possibilities of dipole-dipole interactions in molecular solids. Figure 2.4 illustrates attraction (a) and repulsion (b) between diatomic molecules. The extent of the interaction depends on the magnitude of the dipole moment, which in turn depends on the difference in electronegativity between the two bonded atoms. The largest dipole moments are found for bonds between the more electropositive non-metals (e.g., B, C, H) and strongly electronegative non-metals such as F, O, and N. A few bonds between elements with similar electronegativities have practically zero dipole moments (e.g., C—H, P—H).

The calculation of the force between two simple diatomic dipoles is based on the inverse square law of attraction between individual poles. If these are distance r apart, the force between them is proportional to r^{-2}. Repulsive forces from the opposite end of the dipole must be allowed for, and it turns out that the potential energy of attraction between two dipoles, with moments μ_A and μ_B, is proportional to $\mu_A \mu_B r^{-6} T^{-1}$. In practice, it appears that dipole-dipole interactions are weak forces, much less dependent on molecular weight than are London forces. Table 2.2 compares the experimental melting points of solid interhalogen compounds with the values obtained by interpolating the data given for dihalogens in Table 2.1.

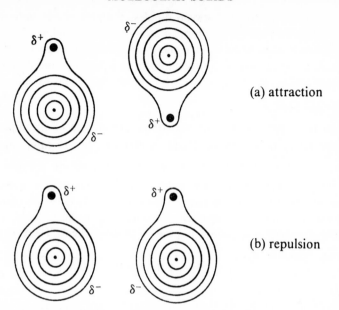

(a) attraction

(b) repulsion

Fig. 2.4. Diagrammatic representation of dipole-dipole forces be-tween two hydrogen chloride molecules: ● = *proton,* · = *Cl nucleus,* ——— = *electron density contours.*

Table 2.2

Melting points of interhalogen compounds

Compound	mol. wt.	m.p.°K observed	m.p.°K interpolated
FCl	54·5	119	112
FBr	99	240	202
BrCl	115·5	219	218
ICl	164	287/300*	272
IBr	208·5	315	327

* Two polymorphic forms.

It can be seen that the observed melting point is significantly higher than the interpolated value only for FBr and ICl, which have the greatest differences in electronegativity between their constituent atoms.

In addition to forces between dipoles, a dipole μ can induce a separation of charges in a non-polar atom or covalent bond of polarizability α, leading to a potential energy of attraction proportional to $\alpha\mu^2 r^{-6}$. It is not easy to test what effect this dipole/induced dipole interaction has on solid properties, but it is thought to be a small one.

Hydrogen bonding

The hydrogen bond is an important special case of the dipole-dipole interaction between F—H, —OH or $\geq$N—H (and rarely $\geq$C—H) and another electronegative atom. It arises on account of the unique properties of the proton, which is much smaller than all other atoms. Two electronegative atoms, usually F, O, or N, can be bonded together by an interaction involving 2–10 kcals mole^{-1} of potential energy if a proton is present between them. There is no

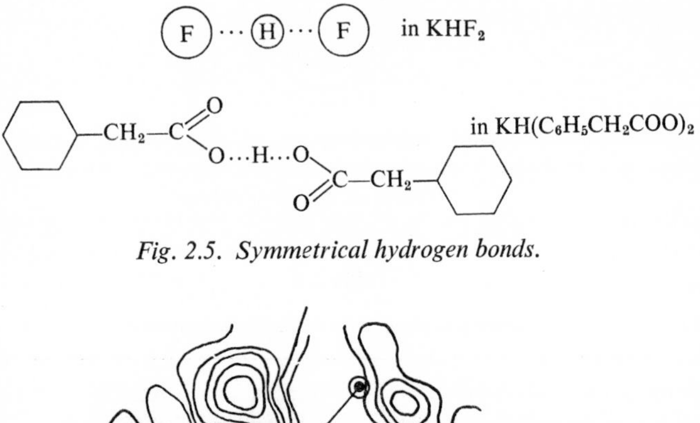

$$\textcircled{F} \cdots \textcircled{H} \cdots \textcircled{F} \quad \text{in KHF}_2$$

$$\text{—CH}_2\text{—C} \overset{\displaystyle O}{\underset{\displaystyle O \cdots H \cdots O}{}} \text{C—CH}_2\text{—} \quad \text{in KH(C}_6\text{H}_5\text{CH}_2\text{COO)}_2$$

Fig. 2.5. Symmetrical hydrogen bonds.

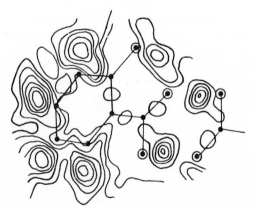

Fig. 2.6. Electron density contours in salicylic acid, $C_6H_4(OH)COOH$, with the contributions due to carbon and oxygen atoms subtracted out: $\bullet = C$, $\odot = O$; positions of hydrogens can be inferred from remaining contours. Note two unsymmetrical $O \cdot\cdot H \cdot\cdot\cdot\cdot O$ bonds. From X-ray diffraction work by Cochran (1953).

satisfactory theory of this interaction, but it appears that the attraction of the non-protonated atom for the proton exceeds the repulsion between the two negatively charged atoms. The resulting hydrogen bond is usually asymmetrical, in which case it can be detected by its infra-red spectrum, but in a few of the strongest interactions, e.g., the HF_2^- ion, it is symmetrical (Fig. 2.5). The position of the proton can often be found from neutron diffraction or careful X-ray diffraction studies (Fig. 2.6). These studies also show that hydrogen bonding leads to a decrease in the distance between H-bonded atoms below that found for the same atoms held together by Van der Waals forces alone (Table 2.3).

Table 2.3

Interatomic distances in Å and hydrogen bonds

Pairs of atoms	Chemical single bond	Symmetrical H-bond	Unsymmetrical H-bond	Van der Waals bond
F—F	1·42	2·26	2·55	⩾2·87
O—O	1·49	2·54	2·76	⩾3·30
N—N	1·47	not known	3·38	⩾3·95

Finally, it appears that atoms forming hydrogen bonds are *oriented* so that the axis of the bond coincides with the axis of a lone pair on the non-protonated atom.

The influence of hydrogen bonds on the properties of molecular solids is immense. The effects include an increase in binding energy, melting point, hardness, and brittleness, and a decrease in compressibility. In addition, the dielectric constant may be abnormally high.

Table 2.4 shows the influence of hydrogen bonding on the melting points of simple hydrides of Groups V, VI, and VII.

Table 2.4

Melting points of hydrides of Groups V, VI, and VII (°K)

Hydride	m.p.	Hydride	m.p.	Hydride	m.p.
HF	190	H_2O	273	H_3N	195
HCl	162	H_2S	190	H_3P	141
HBr	187	H_2Se	209	H_3As	159
HI	222	H_2Te	225	H_3Sb	185

The melting points of HF, H_2O, and H_3N are unusually high considering their low molecular weights. The extent to which the melting point is raised depends on the number of hydrogen bonds which are formed in the solid, and this factor also determines whether the molecules are linked in one-, two-, or three-dimensional infinite arrays by H-bonds. For example, solid HF consists of infinite chains of molecules linked by H-bonds (Fig. 2.7), while ice has an infinite three-dimensional array of water molecules each of which is involved in four H-bonds with neighbouring molecules (Fig. 2.8). As a result, ice is a stronger,

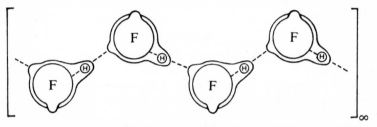

Fig. 2.7. Structure of solid hydrogen fluoride: the FFF angle is 120°, and each molecule is held by two H-bonds. Lone pairs are indicated diagrammatically.

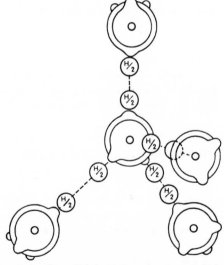

Fig. 2.8. Structure of ice. While H_2O molecules would be found at any one instant of time, the probability of finding a proton in an equilibrium site is 0·5. The OOO angle is 109° 28′, and each molecule is held by four H-bonds.

higher-melting solid than is hydrogen fluoride. Other examples include:

finite structures: organic carboxylic acids, which form dimers involving two H-bonds, e.g.,

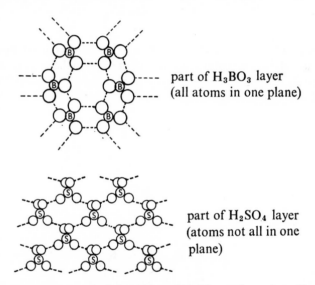

infinite chains: solid HF, β-oxalic acid, and probably nitric acid;

infinite layers: α-oxalic acid, boric acid, sulphuric acid (Fig. 2.9);

infinite three-dimensional arrays: ice, orthophosphoric acid.

part of H_3BO_3 layer
(all atoms in one plane)

part of H_2SO_4 layer
(atoms not all in one plane)

Fig. 2.9. Structures of solid H_3BO_3 and H_2SO_4; each consists of layers of molecules held together by H-bonds: H atoms omitted, ○ = O, Ⓑ = B, Ⓢ = S, ----- = H-bond.

Some of the infinite layer structures, such as boric acid crystals, show unusually perfect cleavage and pronounced anisotropy, as might be expected.

The fluorine bond

This is another special type of dipole-dipole interaction, less common than the hydrogen bond but worth mentioning in this brief survey. It is found experimentally that a small number of fluorides, which are known to be molecular solids, have melting points similar to or higher than the corresponding chlorides. Some examples are collected in Table 2.5.

Table 2.5

Comparison of melting points of some molecular fluorides and chlorides

MF_n	m.p.°K	MCl_n	m.p.°K
AsF_3	265	$AsCl_3$	265
SbF_3	565	$SbCl_3$	346
SiF_4	183	$SiCl_4$	203
GeF_4	236	$GeCl_4$	224

X-ray diffraction studies have shown that in silicon tetrafluoride the molecules are oriented as shown in Fig. 2.10, so that a weak dipole

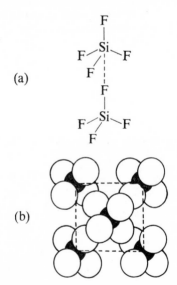

Fig. 2.10. Structure of SiF₄: (a) showing interaction of two molecules, (b) projected along a cube axis of the unit cell; ○ = F, ● = Si.

bond is probably responsible for the relatively high melting point. The pentafluorides of many transition metals (V, Nb, Ta, Cr, Mo, Tc, Re, Ru, and Os) are also associated in the solid state. These compounds probably all exist as tetrameric rings of structure $(-F_4M-F\ldots)_4$ in the solid, and the liquids are also highly viscous and associated.

Electron overlap

This is a form of interaction which has been found in polycyclic aromatic hydrocarbons and some of their derivatives. It can be understood by considering the electron density of a simple aromatic hydrocarbon such as naphthalene, $C_{10}H_8$. In this molecule there are ten electrons in excess of the classical single-bonded structure, and it is believed that these occupy pi-orbitals which extend a considerable distance above and below the plane containing the carbon atoms. In solid hydrocarbons of this type the molecules are stacked with

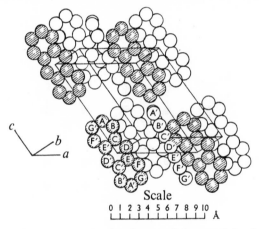

Fig. 2.11. Crystal structure of anthracene (after Cruikshank, 1956).

these planes parallel, so that it is possible for the pi-electron clouds to overlap (Fig. 2.11). Any overlapping means that electrons may be exchanged between molecules and bind them together, but of course this binding force is opposed by electrostatic repulsion between the negatively charged electron clouds. Some indication of the forces involved may be obtained by comparing the melting points of polycyclic aromatic rings with their aliphatic homologues, as is done in Table 2.6.

The increase in melting point with the number of aromatic rings in the molecule is further illustrated by the case of hexabenzocoronene (Fig. 2.12), whose melting point exceeds 970°K, which is the highest known for any molecular solid.

Solid polycyclic aromatic hydrocarbons are usually strongly

Table 2.6

Melting points of molecular solids containing aromatic and aliphatic rings

Aromatic compound	m.p.°K	Aliphatic compound	m.p.°K
Benzene, C_6H_6	278·5	Cyclohexane, C_6H_{12}	279
Naphthalene, $C_{10}H_8$	353	Decalin, $C_{10}H_{18}$	222/241*
Anthracene, $C_{14}H_{10}$	490	Perhydroanthracene, $C_{14}H_{24}$	334/366*

* Two polymorphic forms.

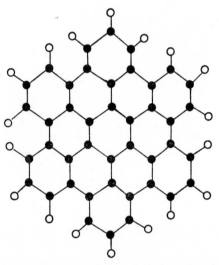

Fig. 2.12. Arrangement of atoms in hexabenzocoronene: $\bullet = C$, $\circ = H$.

anisotropic, and may exhibit properties such as semiconduction, photoconduction, strong absorption in the ultra-violet or visible region, fluorescence, and phosphorescence, some of which are discussed below.

Dissolution of molecular solids

The best general rule in selecting solvents for molecular solids is that of 'like dissolves like'. Thus non-polar molecules usually dissolve best in non-polar solvents such as hydrocarbons or carbon tetrachloride, while polar molecules need polar solvents such as ethers, alcohols, or water. Molecules containing —O—H groups or $>$N—H groups are nearly all soluble in water, and many of them dissolve in liquid HF or liquid ammonia, but they rarely dissolve at all in non-polar solvents. In these cases, the loss of binding energy has to be compensated by a gain in solvation energy of the molecules, both quantities being determined largely by hydrogen bonds. The larger polycyclic aromatic hydrocarbons, such as anthracene, are only moderately soluble in petroleum ether and other non-polar solvents, but dissolve readily in other aromatic solvents such as benzene or pyridine.

Optical properties of molecular solids

Molecular spectra are not much affected by phase transitions. The electronic, vibrational, and rotational spectra, observed respectively in the ultra-violet and visible, near infra-red, and microwave regions, are not greatly changed when a molecular solid is melted or vaporized, with a few exceptions.

A small number of molecular solids change colour during or near phase transitions. For example, solid sulphur, which is yellow, melts to a yellow liquid at 119°C and turns dark red on heating to 159°C. These effects are always caused by chemical decomposition; another example is the heating of solid N_2O_4, which dissociates to give the intensely coloured radical $\cdot NO_2$.

Vibrational energies and frequencies may be up to 5 per cent lower in solids than in the gas phase, owing to intermolecular forces. Molecules which form strong H-bonds, such as HF, H_2O, and NH_3, often have additional infra-red spectral lines in condensed phases. The vibrational energies associated with the lattice itself, as opposed to its constituent molecules, are in the far infra-red region and so are difficult to observe. The number of lattice vibrations can be predicted if the size of the unit cell has been found by X-ray diffraction. If a unit cell contains q molecules, each of which contains p atoms, the number of lattice vibrations is $3q(p-2)$.

Rotational fine structure of vibrational lines is seldom observed in solids as the lines are less sharp than in gases. It is unlikely that free rotation is at all common in solids, but many molecular solids have high temperature forms in which the molecules can oscillate; all rotation is inhibited in low temperature forms.

Fluorescence and phosphorescence are characteristic of polycyclic aromatic hydrocarbons. For example, anthracene fluoresces blue on exposure to ultra-violet light, but its fluorescence is very sensitive to traces of impurities, and is thought to involve the excitation of pi-electrons.

Electrical properties of molecular solids

Almost all molecular solids are insulators, with dielectric constants which vary from values close to unity for non-polar substances to 81 for ice at 273°K. The latter contains highly polar molecules which can readily orient themselves in opposition to an applied electric field, though this power of orientation is lost if the field is alternated with a frequency exceeding 10^{12} cycles sec^{-1}.

Polycyclic aromatic hydrocarbons are unusual in that they exhibit *semiconduction*, that is, they are poor conductors of electricity whose conductivity increases exponentially as the temperature is raised. The conductivity increases dramatically if impurities are present, e.g., sources of electrons like metallic Na, or electron acceptors like I_2. The current is supposed to be carried by pi-electrons, which move freely within the molecules, but which only rarely jump from molecule to molecule by thermal excitation. These substances also exhibit *photoconduction*, that is, they conduct electricity when exposed to light of energy exceeding some critical value, which may be either ultra-violet or visible light. Thus anthracene, which is normally an insulator with a conductivity of 10^{-18} ohm^{-1} cm^{-1}, becomes electrically conducting when exposed to light of energy exceeding about 3 eV (wavelength less than 4000 Å). Both types of conductivity are strongly anisotropic, and occur parallel but not perpendicular to the planes of the molecules. At higher energies or shorter wavelengths (> 5.5 eV or < 2250 Å respectively for anthracene) these molecules show the *photoelectric effect*, that is, they emit electrons on exposure to ultra-violet light. Much greater energies are needed to drive electrons out of most other molecules. Apart from the hydrocarbons mentioned, the only other semiconductors known among molecular solids are N_4S_4 and the phthalocyanines.

Magnetic properties of molecular solids

The vast majority of molecular solids are *diamagnetic*, that is, they are repelled by a magnetic field. The very few *paramagnetic* molecular solids, which are attracted by magnetic fields, contain molecules with unpaired electrons which are better known as free radicals. Examples of free radicals include $NO\cdot$, $NO_2\cdot$, $BF_3NO\cdot$, $ClO_2\cdot$, $ClO_3\cdot$, $BrO_2\cdot$, $BrO_3\cdot$ (decomposes above 200°K), and numerous organic derivatives of $\phi_3C\cdot$ and $\phi_2N\cdot$, where $\phi=$phenyl. Most of these dimerize at low temperatures and become diamagnetic.

Molecular compounds

These are some remarkable compounds between pairs of unrelated substances which have the following characteristics:

1. They only exist in the solid state.
2. They are usually non-stoicheiometric and have variable composition.

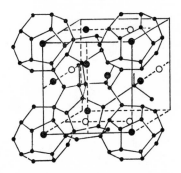

Fig. 2.13. Structure of $Cl_2.5\cdot75H_2O$: $\bullet = Cl_2$, $\cdot = O$, ——— = H-bond. Note dodecahedral cages of water molecules which can trap small molecules (after Barrer, 1964).

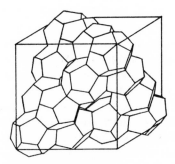

Fig. 2.14. Structure of $Ar.17H_2O$: O atoms at apices of dodecahedra: ——— = H-bond. Each unit cell contains 136 molecules of water and 8 sites which may trap argon atoms (after Barrer, 1964).

X-ray diffraction studies have shown that many of these compounds involve the trapping of the molecules of one substance in the interstices of an open lattice made by the molecules of the other. For example, the substance chlorine hydrate, $Cl_2 . 5\cdot75H_2O$, which is stable below 273°K, contains chlorine molecules trapped in a lattice of water molecules which are held together by hydrogen bonds (Fig. 2.13). It has been shown that water forms hydrates of this kind with many atoms and molecules whose effective diameter lies between 4 and 7 Å. These hydrates are of two types. Small molecules of diameter between

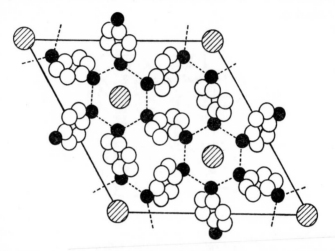

Fig. 2.15. A projection of the 1,4 quinol clathrate structure on its C-face: ● = O, ○ = C, ▨ = lattice gaps which may enclose small atoms or molecules such as Ar or SO_2, ---- = H-bonds, H atoms omitted, —— = outline of face of unit cell (after Wyckoff, 1960).

4 and 5·7 Å, such as Ar, Kr, Cl_2, Br_2, CH_4, PH_3, H_2S, SO_2, N_2O, etc., form hydrates with the ideal formula $X . 5\cdot75H_2O$. Larger molecules, such as CH_3I and $CHCl_3$, can only fit into larger holes in the water lattice and give hydrates with the ideal formula $X . 17H_2O$ (Fig. 2.14). Other examples of this type of compound are formed by lattices of solid phenol or quinol which trap small molecules such as Ar, Kr, Xe, HCl, H_2S, CH_3Br, and CO_2 (Fig. 2.15).

These compounds are collectively known as *inclusion compounds*: when they involve a small molecule trapped in a lattice cage they are called *clathrate compounds*. The two kinds of molecule are only held together by dipole-dipole or other Van der Waals interactions, which may allow more or less free rotation of the trapped molecules. The degree of orientational freedom of a trapped dipolar molecule can be estimated from the dielectric constant of the clathrate. Thus quinol containing CH_3CN has a low dielectric constant, implying that the methyl cyanide molecules are free to rotate; quinol clathrates of CH_3OH have a high dielectric constant, so the methanol molecules are more or less fixed, perhaps by hydrogen bonding.

Some hydrogen bonded solids have interstices which are shaped like long channels rather than closed cages, and these may retain long chain molecules. For example, urea strongly retains n-alkanes on crystallization, while thiourea, which has wider channels, retains

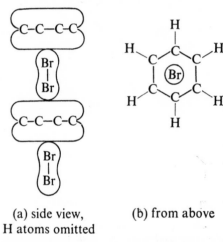

(a) side view,   (b) from above
H atoms omitted

Fig. 2.16. Arrangement of molecules in $Br_2 \cdot C_6H_6$.

branched chain alkanes and some cyclo-alkanes in its lattice. The selectivity of these inclusion processes has given them some technical importance in the separation of hydrocarbons. The well-known starch/iodine and dextrin/iodine compounds are probably examples of this type of inclusion compound. Iodine forms long chain polymers I_n in α-dextrin, with an I–I distance of 3·06 Å, much longer than the 2·66 Å found in I_2 molecules. The I_n chains fit into channels between the dextrin molecules, and the change in bonding of the iodine atoms accounts for the colour change from violet to blue.

Another type of molecular compound is formed by aromatic hydrocarbons and may be stabilized by electron overlap. Examples include the 1:1 compounds of benzene with Cl_2, Br_2 (Fig. 2.16), and

4

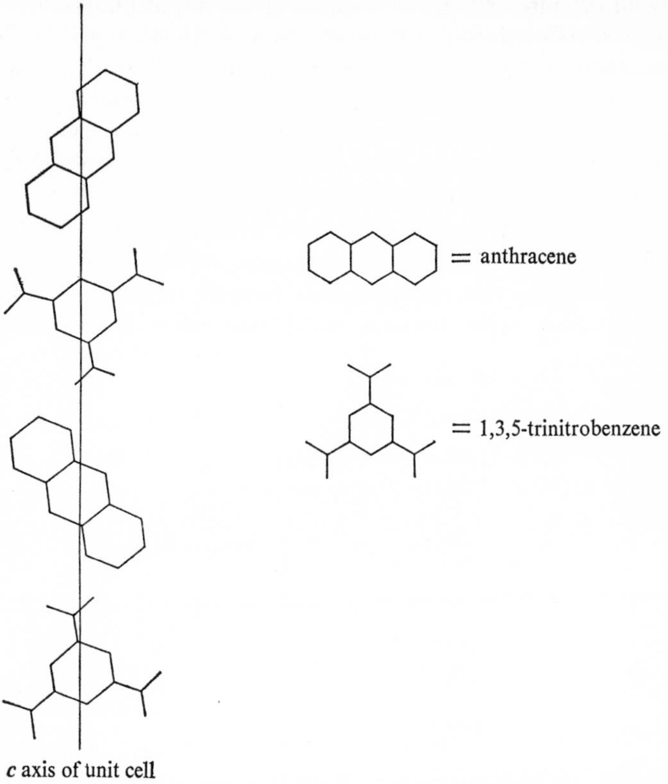

c axis of unit cell

Fig. 2.17. *Structure of 1:1 anthracene/1,3,5-trinitrobenzene molecular compound. The compound is orange, while the constituents are respectively white and yellow. Some pi-bonding occurs between the molecules (after Brown, Wallwork and Wilson, 1964).*

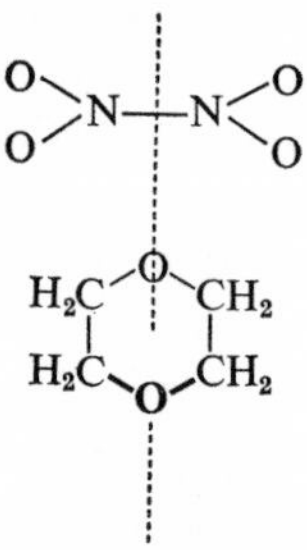

Fig. 2.18. *Geometrical arrangement of dioxan and dinitrogen tetroxide molecules in the compound* $1,4C_4H_8O_2.N_2O_4$: ———— = *covalent bonding,* ---- = *Van der Waals bonding.*

Al_2Br_6. In the case of some compounds involving two aromatic hydrocarbons or their derivatives, such as the 1:1 compound of anthracene with 1,3,5 trinitrobenzene, X-ray diffraction has shown that the aromatic rings are oriented to give the maximum overlap of pi-electrons in the solid state (Fig. 2.17).

Recently, a 1:1 compound of dioxan with dinitrogen tetroxide has been investigated and shown to be a linear polymer of the units shown in Fig. 2.18. It is not clear what type of Van der Waals interaction stabilizes this unusual structure.

3. Covalent solids

A *covalent bond* involves the sharing of two electrons by a pair of atoms. *Covalent solids*, as defined here, are those in which the constituent atoms are linked by an infinite chain, net, or lattice of covalent bonds in one, two, or three dimensions. While the covalent bonds themselves are strong, they only confer strength and resistance to compression in the directions in which they occur. Hence the mechanical properties of covalent solids depend markedly on whether the covalent bonds extend in one, two, or three dimensions.

One-dimensional covalent solids are usually soft or elastic materials, with marked anisotropy if the chain molecules are oriented in a particular direction. For example, on compressing tellurium, the crystal *expands* along the axis of the chain molecules and contracts normally along the other two crystal axes. These substances have relatively low melting points or sublimation points, but frequently decompose on heating. However, many of them can be melted or dissolved in suitable solvents without degrading the long molecules they contain.

The majority of organic solids in this class form amorphous solids; well-known examples include polythene, polyvinyl chloride, and rubber, but these are at least partly crystalline, and the degree of order can be greatly increased by stretching the sample. Inorganic solids may also be largely amorphous (e.g., plastic sulphur and the rubbery $(PNCl_2)_n$), but many are crystalline. Examples, some of whose structures are shown in Fig. 3.1, include:

Se (grey form), Te.
$BeCl_2$, $PdCl_2$, $SiCl_2$, $SiBr_2$, AuI.

SeO_2, β-SO_3, As_2O_3, Sb_2O_3.
SiS_2, Bi_2S_3, Mo_2S_3, Sb_2S_3.
$AgCN$, $AuCN$, $AgSCN$.
$Be(CH_3)_2$, $C_6H_5B.NC_4H_9$.

In some of these the chains are kept rigidly straight by the covalent bonds (e.g., $PdCl_2$, SiS_2), while in others some degree of coiling and/or twisting of the chains is possible (e.g., Se, SeO_2).

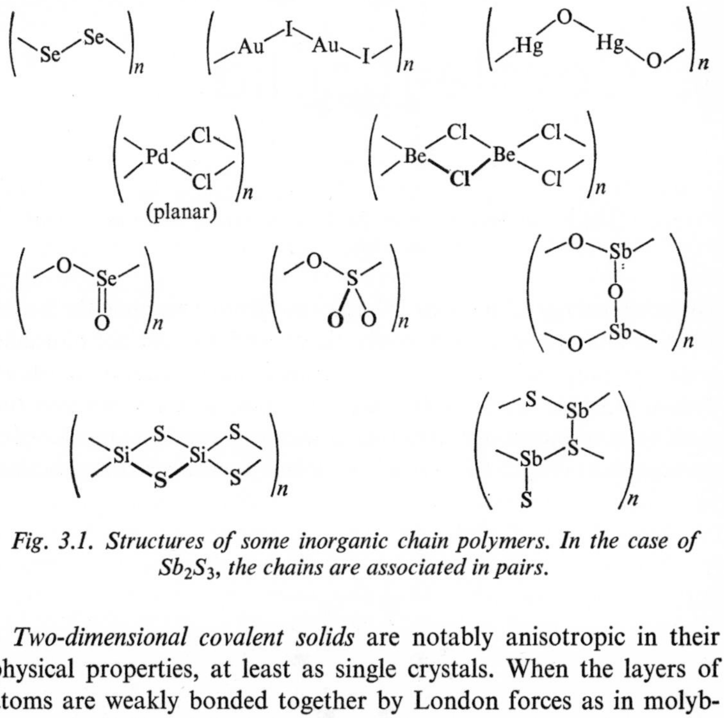

Fig. 3.1. *Structures of some inorganic chain polymers. In the case of Sb_2S_3, the chains are associated in pairs.*

Two-dimensional covalent solids are notably anisotropic in their physical properties, at least as single crystals. When the layers of atoms are weakly bonded together by London forces as in molybdenum disulphide (Fig. 3.2), or by pi-electron overlap as in graphite (Fig. 1.12), they are able to slip over one another and the substances are used as solid lubricants. No lubricating properties are found when the layers are held together by large numbers of hydrogen bonds, as in many metallic hydroxides such as $Al(OH)_3$.

All these materials are fairly compressible perpendicular to the layers, but highly incompressible in the plane of the layers. None of them melts readily, since melting must involve the breaking of many covalent bonds, and the binding energy is large. Graphite is exceptional in having a sublimation point of 3925°K. None of these solids dissolves in any solvent without more or less profound chemical decomposition. In practice, this means that some of them, such as graphite, boron nitride, and red and black phosphorus, are insoluble in nearly all solvents. Others, such as many anhydrous metal halides, sulphides, and hydroxides, dissolve in water or acids with ionization, since the

Fig. 3.2. A portion of the MoS_2 structure viewed in the plane of the layers, which are held together by London forces between S atoms: $\bullet = Mo$, $\circ = S$.

solvation energy of the ions is large enough to overcome the loss of binding in the solid. Alternatively, they may form solvated molecules with less polar solvents. Ferric chloride is an instructive and fairly typical example. In the solid state this exists as a layered structure with six chlorine atoms surrounding each iron atom in an octahedral arrangement (Fig. 3.3). The iron-chlorine bonds are best described

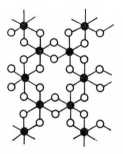

Fig. 3.3. Structure of part of $FeCl_3$ layer: $\bullet = Fe$, $\circ = Cl$.

as polar covalent, while the layers are held together by London forces and dipole–dipole interactions. When heated, ferric chloride boils at 588°K to give Fe_2Cl_6 molecules, which are completely decomposed to $FeCl_3$ molecules above 1000°K. On dissolution in water it forms the ions $Fe(OH_2)_6^{3+} + 3Cl^-$, while on dissolution in ether it forms the solvated complex $Et_2O.FeCl_3$, where Et stands for the ethyl radical. All the different forms have quite different properties. In this particular case, the structure of the solid has little relevance to the chemistry of the substance as usually handled.

The more stable two-dimensional covalent solids are able to form non-stoicheiometric inclusion compounds by diffusion of small atoms or molecules between the layers. In the case of graphite, such compounds have been obtained with alkali metals, bromine, oxygen, sulphuric acid, and other oxyacids, aluminium chloride, and many similar halides, CrO_3, MoO_3, CuS, PbS, FeS_2, and many other substances. The layers of carbon atoms move farther apart when these compounds are formed, decreasing the density of the solid. Thus graphite oxides have been made with interlayer spacings of between 6 and 11 Å, compared with the 3·35 Å spacing in graphite itself. In the same way boron nitride (BN) can take up ferric and aluminium chlorides between its layers, while molybdenum disulphide absorbs alkali metals from liquid ammonia, and zinc hydroxide forms intercalated compounds with nitrophenol.

Examples of two-dimensional covalent solids include: black phosphorus (Fig. 1.13) and arsenic; graphite (Fig. 1.12) and its analogue boron nitride; graphite fluoride (CF), which has layers containing cyclohexanoid rather than aromatic rings; many anhydrous metal halides of formula MHa_2 or MHa_3, for example cadmium chloride (Fig. 3.4) and ferric chloride (Fig. 3.3); many metal sulphides of formula MS or M_2S_3, and also MoS_2 and WS_2; and many metal hydroxides and hydrous oxides of formula $M(OH)_2$, $M(OH)_3$, or MO_2H. Some of these might be better classed as semiconductors.

Three-dimensional covalent solids are very hard, incompressible substances. Their melting points are very high, if melting can be said to occur for this type of solid, since the process must involve breaking most of the covalent bonds holding the lattice together. Although most of them can be made to dissolve in a few reagents, dissolution involves profound chemical changes, so that reprecipitation from a solvent is rarely possible. Only one three-dimensional solid is both covalent and non-polar according to our definition, and that is diamond, which has the structure shown in Fig. 1.12. Silicon and germanium, which have similar structures, are both semiconductors and will be discussed in chapter 6. Diamond is the hardest known substance, though borazon (BN) and titanium boride (TiB_2) are perhaps equally hard. Diamond is also highly incompressible, very inert, and difficult to dissolve, and has a sublimation temperature exceeding $3700°K$. At NTP it is thermodynamically unstable with respect to graphite, but its rate of transition to the latter form is negligibly low. Its density of 3·51, compared with 2·22 for graphite, shows that it should be the stable form at high pressures (Fig. 1.7). It has been predicted that at very high pressures, exceeding 600 kbars, an even denser, metallic form of carbon, with close-packed atoms, should be stable.

Most of the other three-dimensional covalent solids are polar and have semiconducting properties, e.g., silicon carbide, SiC, and

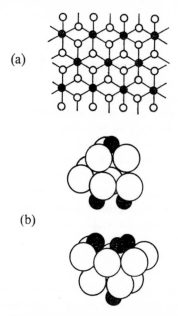

(a)

(b)

Fig. 3.4. (a) part of a CdCl₂ layer, showing covalent bonds, (b) perspective drawing of adjacent parts of two layers, held together by long Cd—Cd bonds: ● = Cd, ○ = Cl.

borazon, the high pressure form of BN. Polarity and semiconduction are independent attributes of solids. Thus elementary silicon is non-polar and semiconducting, while silicon dioxide or silica is strongly polar and a good insulator. According to some workers, the bonds in silica are 60 per cent covalent and 40 per cent ionic, but experimental techniques for measuring the percentage ionic character of bonds are still far from full development. Since the bonds are tetrahedrally oriented around each silicon atom, they are best described as polar covalent bonds. In practice, silica has the properties of a three-dimensional covalent solid. It has several polymorphic forms, of which amorphous silica and quartz (Fig. 3.5) have great technical importance.

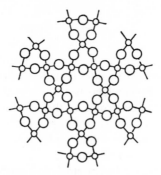

Fig. 3.5. Structure of β-quartz projected on to a plane: ○ = Si, ○ = O; each Si is surrounded by a tetrahedron of four O atoms.

Optical properties of covalent solids

Good insulators, such as diamond and silica, are transparent in the visible and near ultra-violet regions, while semiconductors such as silicon and germanium, and many metallic sulphides, undergo electronic excitation in the near infra-red region, and are opaque with some metallic lustre in the visible region. Graphite, with its large number of mobile pi-electrons, is notably opaque and absorbs throughout the visible region. On the other hand, two of its derivatives, graphite fluoride (CF) and graphite oxide, are white or transparent, which is evidence that the pi-electrons are not mobile, implying that the carbon rings in these compounds are cyclohexanoid and not aromatic as in graphite itself. Covalent sulphides of metals often have quite different absorption spectra and colours from ionic derivatives. Compare white ZnS, yellow CdS, and black or red HgS, with colourless ZnF_2, CdF_2, and HgF_2.

Vibration spectra in the infra-red region should only be observed for polar solids, such as silica. In practice, many diamonds absorb infra-red radiation weakly at about 0·15 eV, where there is a forbidden band which may arise from impurities. The lattice vibrations in the far infra-red region mostly await investigation. These vibrations have low energies, but may be studied by measuring the inelastic scattering of neutrons, electrons, or X-rays of low energy. Vibration and rotation spectra should occur for one-dimensional covalent solids if the chain molecules have some freedom.

Thermal properties

The thermal conductivity of diamond is $1\cdot6$ cal sec^{-1} cm^{-1} deg^{-1}, which is the highest conductivity for any substance at NTP. Diamond is a better conductor of heat than metallic copper. The heat is conducted by the lattice vibrations of diamond, which are readily propagated in the nearly perfect crystal. Theory shows that thermal conductivity should be inversely related to atomic weight, so that carbon should conduct heat better than does silicon, as is found to be the case. Graphite also conducts heat fairly well, but in this case the conductivity is highly anisotropic, as the heat is conducted mainly by the pi-electrons which are only mobile parallel to the layers of carbon atoms. Most other covalent solids are less good thermal conductors than these two exceptional substances.

Silica is remarkable for its extremely low coefficient of expansion, which is made use of in apparatus which has to be resistant to thermal strains. This can be correlated with the fact that its lattice vibrations are almost perfectly harmonic, which is certainly not true for the majority of solids.

Electrical properties

Diamond is one of the best electrical insulators known, as it has a resistivity of about 10^{22} ohm cm. This implies that a large amount of energy is needed to excite electrons in the carbon–carbon bonds to a state where they can conduct electricity. The amount of energy is about $5\cdot4$ eV, corresponding to the absorption band which all diamonds have at a wavelength of 2250 Å in the ultra-violet region. On the other hand, graphite is a good conductor of electricity as no energy is needed to excite the conduction electrons in its pi-orbitals, and it is used for the electrodes in dry batteries and electrolytic cells of all kinds. Using single crystals of graphite it can be shown that the resistivity is 10^{-4} ohm cm parallel to the layers of carbon atoms and $2\cdot5$ ohm cm perpendicular to these layers. This anisotropy is readily understood if it is assumed that the pi-electrons carry the current. The conductivity parallel to the layers is equivalent to metallic conductivity, and like that of metals, it decreases as the temperature is raised.

Other covalent solids have electrical resistivities intermediate between those of graphite and diamond. Substances with a resistivity greater than 10^{9} ohm cm are generally known as insulators, and include silica, boron nitride (both forms), and graphite fluoride in this group. Substances with a resistivity between 10^9 and 10^2 ohm cm are called semiconductors and are discussed in chapter 6. Tellurium is anomalous in having a resistivity intermediate between semiconductors and metals (Fig. 5.7); it is sometimes called a semi-metal.

Polar covalent solids may be piezoelectric or pyroelectric. These properties, like optical activity, are only found in crystals which have no centre of symmetry, e.g., the low temperature form of silica known as α-quartz. If such a crystal is deformed by applying a stress, the dipoles in it are displaced asymmetrically, so that two opposite faces of the crystal develop electrical charges of opposite sign. The separation of electrical charges by compressing a crystal is called *piezoelectricity*. Conversely, if an electric field is applied to a crystal which has no centre of symmetry, the dipoles in it are displaced, causing strain which can be detected by observations in polarized light. If a piezoelectric crystal is exposed to an electrical field of alternating polarity, the dipoles constantly re-orient themselves to keep pace with the changing field. Usually they lag behind the field, but for any given crystal a frequency exists at which the dipoles change their orientation in phase with the field. This is called the *resonance frequency* for the crystal, and is so sharply defined for quartz crystals that the latter are used as frequency standards.

Similar effects occur when a crystal lacking a centre of symmetry is heated. The thermal expansion is anisotropic, so the dimensions of the crystal change unequally and two opposite faces develop charges of opposite sign. This is the *pyroelectric effect*. Conversely, pyroelectric solids become hot when exposed to strong electric fields.

Magnetic properties

Covalent solids are all normally diamagnetic, as they contain electrons linked in pairs with oppositely-directed magnetic moments. Paramagnetic properties can be induced by heating, or by bombardment with energetic radiation such as electrons, X-rays, or gamma rays. Electrons with unpaired magnetic moments may then be trapped in the lattice and give rise to permanent paramagnetism at room temperature or below. For example, soot, which consists of finely divided impure graphite, is paramagnetic and is used as a secondary reference standard for some magnetic measurements. Paramagnetism in covalent solids can usually be annealed out by heating until the electrons of unpaired spin become mobile, meet and combine, followed by cooling to a suitable temperature.

Inclusion compounds

When nickel cyanide is crystallized in the presence of ammonia and benzene, the cubic lattice formed contains large holes which are able to trap benzene molecules, as shown in Fig. 3.6. Other inclusion compounds have been discussed above.

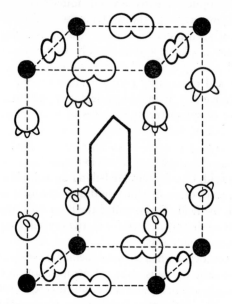

Fig. 3.6. Unit crystal cell of Ni(CN)$_2$NH$_3$.C$_6$H$_6$.

● = Ni, ⊙ = NH$_3$, ∞ = CN, ⬡ = C$_6$H$_6$.

The Ni(CN)$_2$ layers are held together by NH$_3$ molecules co-ordinated to nickel, and the benzene rings fit into the interstices.

4. Ionic solids

Typical ionic solids contain discrete charged ions separated by regions of negligible electron density. These ions are held together by strong electrostatic forces, which account for the large binding energies, high melting points, hardness, and incompressibility of ionic solids. The simplest examples of ionic solids are the compounds formed by electropositive metals, such as potassium or barium, with electronegative non-metals such as fluorine or oxygen. Such compounds mostly contain simple, monatomic ions which pack together as if they were spheres of different sizes. Hence the crystal structures of these substances are fairly simple, as they are determined by two factors: the maintenance of electrical neutrality and the relative sizes of the ions.

The requirement for electrical neutrality means that simple ionic solids should be perfectly stoicheiometric, because any departure from stoicheiometry would lead to the development of electrical charge, which is not observed. Imperfections involving minor departures from stoicheiometry are found in real crystals and can be induced in ionic crystals, but they are associated with abnormal colours, luminescence, and conduction properties and can be annealed out by heating. These are discussed in chapter 6.

The type of crystal structure is determined mainly by the packing of the larger ion, which is usually the anion. The oppositely charged ions are sometimes small enough to fit into the interstices between the larger ions. If the two ions are about the same size, they form a mixed, close-packed lattice. From purely geometrical considerations one can draw up a list of the ways in which two sets of spheres of radius

r_1 and r_2 should pack together. The critical parameter is the *radius ratio*, r_1/r_2. For example, consider the ionic solids of formula MX, where M represents the metallic cation and X the anion. These include the well-known salts NaCl and CaO, together with less well known materials such as LiRe, CsAu, ScN, and ThC. The *co-ordination number* (C.N.) of an ion is defined as the number of ions of opposite sign which immediately surround it. In ionic solids of formula MX,

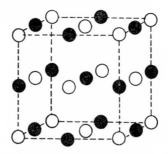

Fig. 4.1. The sodium chloride unit crystal cell.

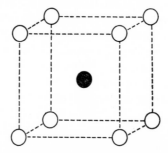

Fig. 4.2. The caesium chloride unit crystal cell: a body-centred cubic structure.

the C.N. of M must equal the C.N. of X. It is the co-ordination number which is so sensitive to changes in the ratio of the radii of M and X, as shown in Table 4.1. The common sodium chloride and caesium chloride structures are illustrated in Figs. 4.1 and 4.2.

The radii of some simple ions according to Wells (1962) are given in Table 4.2. According to both theory and experiment, ions in solids are not perfect spheres and ionic radii are not perfectly additive, so it is not surprising that predictions made about crystal structures from these radii are not always right. For example; KF, RbF and CsF have the

Table 4.1

*Structure, co-ordination number, and radius ratio
of ionic solids MX*

Arrangement of X about M	C.N.	r_M/r_X	Examples
Triangular	3	< 0·225	None known
Tetrahedral	4	< 0·414	BeO; rare
Octahedral	6	< 0·732	NaCl; common
Cubic	8	< 1	CsCl; frequent

Table 4.2

*Radii of some simple ions in Ångstrom units
(after Wells, 1962)*

Anion	Radius	Cation	Radius
Br^-	1·95	Al^{3+}	0·50
Cl^-	1·81	Be^{++}	0·31
F^-	1·36	Ba^{++}	1·35
I^-	2·16	Ca^{++}	0·99
N^{3-}	1·71	Cd^{++}	0·97
O^{--}	1·40	Cs^+	1·69
P^{3-}	2·12	K^+	1·33
S^{--}	1·84	Li^+	0·60
Se^{--}	1·98	Mg^{++}	0·65
		Na^+	0·95
		Pb^{++}	1·21
		Rb^+	1·48
		Sc^{3+}	0·81
		Sr^{++}	1·13
		Ti^{4+}	0·68
		Tl^+	1·44
		Y^{3+}	0·93
		Zn^{++}	0·74
		Zr^{4+}	0·80

sodium chloride structure at NTP, though the caesium chloride structure would have been predicted from their ionic radii. Many ionic solids are polymorphic, showing that the ionic radii depend on temperature. Thus caesium chloride changes to a sodium chloride structure at 718°K.

In the case of ionic solids of formula MX_2 (or M_2X) similar principles apply. Most of the structures are either of the fluorite (Fig. 4.3) or rutile type (Fig. 4.4). In fluorite structures the cation is relatively large ($r_M/r_X > 0.732$), while in rutile structures the cation is small ($0.732 > r_M/r_X > 0.414$). If the cation is very small, as in BeF_2, the cristobalite structure may be found. Solids of formula MX_3 or M_3X rarely have simple structures, but the radius ratio is still a critical parameter.

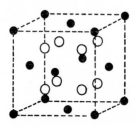

Fig. 4.3. The fluorite unit crystal cell: ● = *cation, e.g.,* Ca^{2+}; ○ = *anion, e.g.,* F^-.

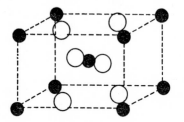

Fig. 4.4. The tetragonal unit crystal cell of rutile: ● = *cation, e.g.,* Ti^{4+}; ○ = *anion, e.g.* O^{2-}.

As a result of their relatively simple structures, most of the simple ionic solids mentioned so far exhibit good cleavage and are not markedly anisotropic. Other types of ionic solids exist which can behave differently and have some new properties. These solids contain *complex ions*, where a complex ion is an electrically charged molecule, that is, it is a collection of atoms linked by covalent bonds which possesses an overall electric charge. Complex ions may be either finite (e.g., sulphate, SO_4^{--}) or infinite in one, two or three dimensions, and each type has certain characteristics which are discussed below.

Solids containing finite complex ions

Many familiar complex ions, such as ammonium (NH_4^+) and perchlorate (ClO_4^-), are nearly spherical in shape and pack into crystals very like simple ions. Others, such as nitrate (NO_3^-) and carbonate (CO_3^{--}), are not spherical and tend to pack with some degree of orientation. In the case of calcite, $CaCO_3$, all the flat carbonate ions pack in parallel planes (Fig. 4.5). As usual, the larger, non-spherical ion determines the structure, with the smaller ion, usually the cation, packing into the interstices. The actual structure taken up may have profound effects on the cleavage and anisotropy of the crystal. For example, calcite cleaves admirably well, but as might be expected the best cleavage planes are parallel to the planes

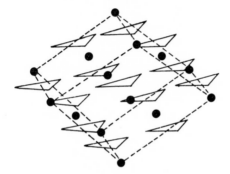

Fig. 4.5. The rhombohedral unit crystal cell of calcite: $\bullet = Ca^{2+}$, $\triangleleft = CO_3^{--}$. Note how all the CO_3^{--} anions are arranged in parallel planes.

of the carbonate ions, and the crystal never splits in such a way as to break the covalent bonds holding the carbonate ions together. Calcite is also well known for its anisotropy. Thus it is doubly refracting, which implies that light travels faster parallel to the planes than it does perpendicular to them; the refractive index varies with the axis of measurement. Again, on heating, a calcite crystal expands along the axis perpendicular to the planes containing the carbonate ions, but contracts along the two axes parallel to these planes. These properties are understandable in terms of the crystal structure.

Crystals containing finite complex ions frequently exist in more than one form. At low temperatures the ions are completely ordered, and on raising the temperature the onset of disorder is marked by a gradual transition analogous to those found in molecular solids such as methane. For example, most ammonium salts have cubic structures which undergo a gradual transition at about 250°K. Each ammonium ion is surrounded by eight anions at the apices of the unit cell, and it can readily be shown that there are two possible equivalent orientations of the tetrahedral ammonium ion for which all four N—H bonds lie along the diagonals of the cube. Above the transition temperature the ammonium cations have one or other of the two possible orientations in a disordered arrangement. Rotation or oscillation of the ion is not involved.

A very large number of finite complex ions are now known. They may be classified as AX_n structures, short chains, ring polymers, and cage structures by analogy with molecules. Some examples are given below. It is noteworthy that nearly all complex ions are anions.

AX_n structures in complex ions

The shapes of these ions are closely related to those of the isoelectronic molecules. The X ligands arrange themselves as far away from one another as possible, with the reservation that if A has one or more lone pairs of electrons these distort the structure from its maximum possible symmetry. Further distortions may arise if A is a transition metal with d-electrons available for bonding, or less

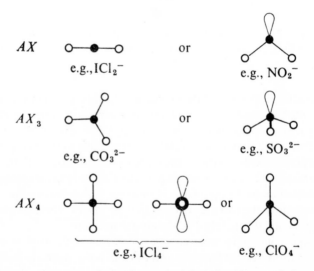

Fig. 4.6. Structures of complex ions of formula AX_n^{m-} with $9 \geqslant n \geqslant 2$. A lone pair of electrons is represented by ◁▷.

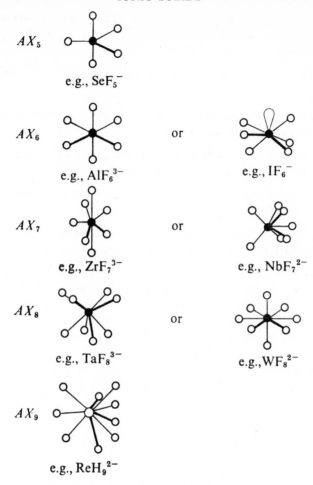

AX_5

e.g., SeF_5^-

AX_6 or

e.g., AlF_6^{3-} e.g., IF_6^-

AX_7 or

e.g., ZrF_7^{3-} e.g., NbF_7^{2-}

AX_8 or

e.g., TaF_8^{3-} e.g., WF_8^{2-}

AX_9

e.g., ReH_9^{2-}

Fig. 4.6.—continued

commonly if X is not an atom from the first period (e.g., silicon). As far as crystal packing is concerned, most AX_n ions are approximately spherical, at least for $n > 3$. Some examples are given in Fig. 4.6.

AX_2 ions may be linear (e.g., UO_2^{++}, CN_2^{--}, and ICl_2^-) or bent (e.g., BrF_2^+, NO_2^-).

AX_3 ions may be planar (e.g., $C(NH_2)_3^+$, CO_3^{--}, and NO_3^-) or pyramidal with a lone pair completing the tetrahedron (e.g., CF_3^-, SO_3^{--}, ClO_3^-).

AX_4 ions may be tetrahedral (e.g., NH_4^+, PCl_4^+, SO_4^{--}, and ClO_4^-) or planar (e.g., ICl_4^-, which has two lone pairs completing the octahedron).

AX_5 ions, which are rare, are trigonal bipyramids (e.g., SbF_5^{--}, SeF_5^-).

AX_6 ions may be octahedral (e.g., AlF_6^{3-}, IO_6^{5-}) or rarely distorted by a lone pair (e.g., $SeBr_6^{--}$, IF_6^-).

AX_7 ions, which are rare, may be pentagonal bipyramids (e.g., ZrF_7^{3-}, UF_7^{3-}) or face-centred trigonal prisms (e.g., NbF_7^{2-}).

AX_8 ions, which are also rare, may be square antiprisms (e.g., TaF_8^{3-}) or dodecahedra (e.g., MoF_8^{--}).

AX_9 ions, which are very rare, may be three-face-centred antiprisms (e.g., $Nd(OH_2)_9^{3+}$) or a double truncated pyramid (e.g., ReH_9^{2-}).

Short chain structures include polymeric elementary ions such as Hg_2^{++}, N_3^-, O_2^{--}, S_2^{--}, S_3^{--}, and I_3^-; dimers such as $N_2H_6^{++}$ and $B_2H_6^{--}$; pyro-salts such as $O(SO_3)_2^{--}$, $O(PO_3)_2^{4-}$, and $O(SiO_3)_2^{6-}$ among which the last is unique in having the SiOSi angle equal to $180°$; a few fluoro-anions such as $F(SbF_3)_2^-$; and peroxy-salts such as $O_3S.OO.SO_3{}^-$ and $O_3P.OO.PO_3^{4-}$.

Ring polymers, some of which are shown in Fig. 4.7, include $(BO_2)_3^{3-}$ in $NaBO_2$, $(SiO_3)_3^{6-}$ in $CaSiO_3$ and $(PO_3)_4^{12-}$ in $AlPO_3$. There

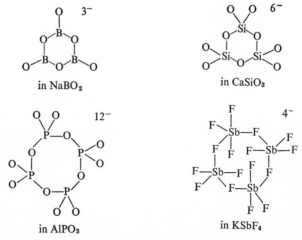

Fig. 4.7. Structures of some ring polymeric anions.

are many more complicated examples among borates, silicates, and phosphates. The only fluoro-anion thought to be of this type is $(SbF_4)_4^{4-}$ in $KSbF_4$.

Cluster structures (see Fig. 4.8) have the octahedral B_6^{--} ion in CaB_6 as a simple example. The cations $Mo_6Cl_8^{4+}$ and $Ta_6Cl_{12}^{++}$ are more complicated, while the heteropolyacids such as $SiMo_6O_{24}^{6-}$ and

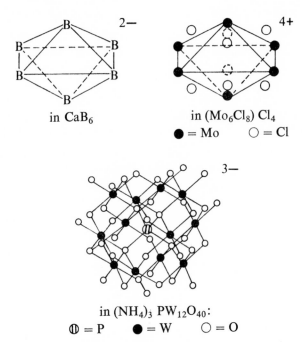

in CaB_6

in $(Mo_6Cl_8)\,Cl_4$

● = Mo   ○ = Cl

in $(NH_4)_3\,PW_{12}O_{40}$:

◍ = P   ● = W   ○ = O

Fig. 4.8. *Structures of some ions with cluster structures.*

$PW_{12}O_{40}^{3-}$ can be extremely complex. The heteropolyacids contain large, pseudospherical ions formed by oxo-derivatives of Mo, W, Nb, or Ta enclosing a central oxo-anion; their salts are mostly insoluble in water. They are interesting because they can be reversibly reduced and oxidized, and have been used as catalysts for hydrocarbon reactions.

Infinite one-dimensional or chain ions

These are not very common, and are frequently decomposed in solution. The majority are only known in solids. Some examples are shown in Fig. 4.9; the more complex chain silicates have not been illustrated. Most of these ions give rise to insoluble salts, some of which have interesting cleavage properties. For example, asbestos contains chain silicate anions which pack together in oriented bundles and which are responsible for its cleavage into fibres.

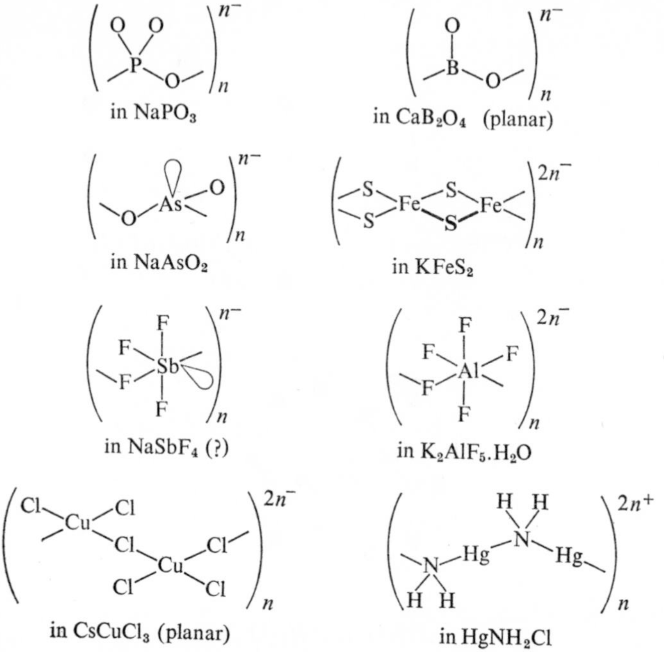

Fig. 4.9. *Structures of some infinite chain ions:* $\bigcirc$ = *lone pair affecting stereochemistry.*

Infinite two-dimensional or layer ions

These are not very common either, but include the cation $(Hg_3(NH)_2)_n^{n+}$ and the anion $(AlF_4)_n^{n-}$ in $TlAlF_4$. The latter contains layers of AlF_6 octahedra each of which shares four corners with its neighbours (Fig. 4.10). Similar structures arise from WO_6 octahedra sharing four corners, or SiO_4 tetrahedra sharing three corners. The latter case leads to layers of composition $(Si_2O_5)_n^{2n-}$, and complex derivatives of this type of layer are found in micas and other silicates. These solids are insoluble and some, such as mica, show nearly perfect cleavage parallel to the layers.

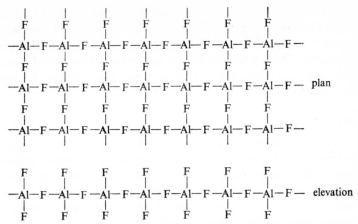

Fig. 4.10. A portion of the infinite layer ion $(AlF_4)_n^{n-}$ *in TlAlF₄, viewed from above and from the side. F atoms above and below each Al atom have been omitted for clarity in the plan view. The Tl⁺ ions are located between the negatively charged layers.*

Infinite three-dimensional ions

A large number of silicate minerals contain three-dimensional silicate anions. Some of these anions are based on an infinite SiO_2 lattice (Fig. 3.5) in which some silicon atoms are replaced by $(K + Al)$ or an equivalent combination. A potassium feldspar, which is a very common mineral, might have the ideal composition $KAlSi_3O_8$, for example. Feldspars are dense minerals without outstanding ion-exchange properties. Other silicates, such as the zeolites (e.g., $KAlSi_2O_6$), are much less dense and have a lattice which contains gaps and channels through which ions and molecules may pass. As a result, they can absorb large amounts of water and also certain gases reversibly. In addition, the potassium they contain can be replaced by other small cations if a solution of the cation in question is allowed to percolate through the mineral. The technical importance of zeolites as water softeners arises from their cation exchange capacity.

The substance known as Millon's base, or Hg_2NOH, and its salts Hg_2NCl and $Hg_2N.NO_3$, contain infinite three-dimensional cations of composition $(Hg_2N)_n^{n+}$, and function as anion exchangers. More important at the present day are organic ion exchangers containing infinite three-dimensional ions. For example, synthetic polymers of styrene ($C_6H_5CH{=}CH_2$) containing sulphonic acid ($-SO_3H$) groups function as cation exchangers, while similar polymers containing trimethylamino ($-N(CH_3)^+_3$) groups function as anion exchangers.

All solids of this type have no definite melting point, since they cannot melt without profound chemical decomposition. In the same way they are insoluble in all solvents which do not attack them chemically. They are therefore inert and resistant to chemical attack other than ion exchange; the silicates are also resistant to high temperatures.

Lattice energies

The *lattice energy* of an ionic solid MX is defined as the energy evolved when M^+ and X^- are brought together in the correct proportions in the vapour phase to form the solid. As defined, the lattice energy cannot be measured in a single experiment, since few or no ionic solids sublime to give free ions. In practice, the lattice energy is obtained by separating the theoretical sublimation

$$\underset{\text{solid}}{MX} \rightarrow \underset{\text{gas}}{M^+} + \underset{\text{gas}}{X^-}$$

into practicable stages, known as the Born–Haber cycle.

$$\underset{\text{solid}}{MX} \rightarrow \begin{cases} \underset{\text{solid}}{M} & \rightarrow \underset{\text{gas}}{M\cdot} & \rightarrow \underset{\text{gas}}{M^+} \\ + & + & + \\ \underset{\text{gas}}{\tfrac{1}{2}X_2} & \rightarrow \underset{\text{gas}}{X\cdot} & \rightarrow \underset{\text{gas}}{X^-} \end{cases}$$

It can readily be deduced that the lattice energy is given by the relation:

Lattice energy of MX = Heat of formation of MX + Heat of sublimation of M + Ionization energy of M + $\frac{1}{2}$ dissociation energy of X_2 − Electron affinity of X.

The quantities on the right-hand side of this equation can all be measured experimentally. An example of the magnitudes involved in the calculation of the lattice energy of sodium chloride from experimental data is given below:

	kcal mole^{-1}
Heat of formation of NaCl	98
Heat of sublimation of Na	25
Ionization energy of Na	118
$\frac{1}{2}$ Dissociation energy of Cl_2	29
Electron affinity of Cl	−88
Lattice energy of NaCl	182

The lattice energy of NaCl may also be calculated from the electrostatic relation

$$E = 1 \cdot 747 \, Ne^2/r$$

where $1 \cdot 747$ is a geometrical factor called the *Madelung constant*, N is Avogadro's number, e the electronic charge, and r the shortest NaCl distance in the solid. If small corrections are made for the compressibility of the ions, their vibrations, and for induced dipolar and London forces, excellent agreement can be obtained with the experimental lattice energies for many simple ionic solids. It turns out, however, that the theoretical lattice energy is not very sensitive to the model chosen for its calculation. This can be seen qualitatively from the fact that the lattice energies of ionic solids are of the same order of magnitude as the binding energies of purely covalent solids such as diamond. The replacement of many ionic interactions in a crystal by covalent ones may not alter the binding energy very much. Hence the agreement between theoretical and experimental lattice energies is not good evidence for the correctness of the ionic model in any particular case.

Ladd and Lee (1964 and 1965) have made a useful tabulation of lattice energies and give an illuminating discussion of them.

Melting and dissolution

Ionic solids which melt without decomposition produce ionized melts, which conduct electricity well. For melting to occur, thermal energy equivalent to the lattice energy must be supplied to the solid. Most ionic solids have lattice energies between 150 and 750 kcals mole^{-1}, and their melting points are mostly between 800 and 2500°K. The lattice entropy, much of which is lost when a solid melts to form a disordered liquid, does not affect melting points to anything like the same extent as does the lattice energy. As explained above, ionic solids containing complex ions may decompose before melting occurs, and therefore sublime at relatively low temperatures. For example, ammonium chloride, which consists of NH_4^+ and Cl^- ions in the solid state, sublimes with decomposition at 613°K to give NH_3 and HCl molecules. Again, phosphorus pentachloride, which consists of PCl_4^+ and PCl_6^- ions in the solid state, sublimes at 432°K to give molecules of PCl_5. Ionic solids containing infinite ions cannot melt in the strict sense of the word. Simple ionic solids rarely or never sublime.

The only ionic solids which can dissolve without chemical decomposition are those containing simple or finite complex ions. For solution to occur, two large energy terms must be balanced; the lattice energy must be less than the sum of the heats of solvation of the ions, if entropy effects are neglected. As a result, ionic solids tend to dissolve in strongly polar solvents such as hydrogen fluoride, water, or liquid ammonia. Here the solvent molecules, being dipoles, can bond more or less strongly to both the anion and the cation, and the high dielectric constant of these solvents is a favourable environment for ions. On the other hand non-polar solvents such as carbon tetrachloride, which have low dielectric constants and little or no affinity for ions, are very poor solvents for ionic solids.

When the lattice energies and solvation energies of ions are known with reasonable accuracy, it is possible to predict the solubilities of ionic solids. For example, Ladd and Lee (1964 and 1965) give the following hydration energies of ions in kcals mole^{-1}: Ca^{++} 386; Ag^+ 117; F^- 116; Cl^- 84; Br^- 76; I^- 67. They also give the lattice energies of the halides of calcium and silver, which are compared with the sums of hydration energies in Table 4.3. Without allowing for

Table 4.3

Lattice energies and solubilities of halides of calcium and silver

Solid	Lattice energy kcal mole^{-1}		Sum of hydration energies of ions; kcal mole^{-1}	Solubility in water
CaF_2	619	>	618	Insoluble
$CaCl_2$	531	<	554	Soluble
$CaBr_2$	510	<	538	Soluble
CaI_2	488	<	520	Soluble
AgF	226	<	233	Soluble
AgCl	214	>	201	Insoluble
AgBr	211	>	193	Insoluble
AgI	208	>	184	Insoluble

entropy differences, the data coincide with the experimental findings on solubilities, which at first sight seem paradoxical. We can say that calcium fluoride is insoluble because of its large lattice energy. Silver chloride, bromide, and iodide are insoluble because of the small hydration energies of their constituent ions, while the fluoride is soluble because of the exceptionally large hydration energy of the fluoride anion.

Spectra of ionic solids

All ionic solids absorb in the ultra-violet region, and in some cases the absorption extends into the visible region. These electronic spectra usually consist of broad bands with a number of fairly sharp peaks, but the absorption is rarely so intense in the visible region as to render the crystals opaque. Coloured ionic solids can be divided into three classes:

1. Those containing coloured ions, which give similarly coloured solutions, so that their spectra do not alter greatly on dissolution, e.g., Fe^{3+}, MnO_4^-. The colour is usually due to electronic transitions involving the d-electrons of transition metals, or the f-electrons of lanthanides and actinides which give more or less sharp line spectra.

2. Those containing ions which are normally colourless in solution. For example, Ag^+, PO_4^{3-}, and AsO_4^{3-} are colourless ions, but Ag_3PO_4 is yellow and Ag_3AsO_4 is red. The colour is caused by the distortion of the electron shells of one ion by the other in the crystal, and is most marked for highly polarizable ions which are easily distorted, such as sulphides and iodides. In many cases the distortion is so great that the bond between anion and cation is better described as a polar covalent bond.

3. Those containing metal ions in two distinct valency states. The solid compounds of this type are usually insoluble and intensely coloured. They are rare, but have empirical formulae implying an unusual valency, e.g., red Mn_3O_4 and Pb_3O_4; black Fe_3O_4 and Co_3O_4; dark green U_3O_8; blue $KFe(Fe(CN)_6)$; black $Cs_2Au(AuCl_6)$, and violet $Rb_4[Sb^{III}Br_6][Sb^VBr_6]$. The intense colour is thought to be caused by electrons hopping from one metal atom to the other at high frequencies.

Ionic solids also absorb strongly in the infra-red region, since they are highly polar. If the unit cell contains n atoms, the infra-red spectrum should consist of $3n-3$ bands. For example, caesium chloride has two atoms per unit cell and has three infra-red bands. Some simple ionic solids are transparent in the near infra-red, and are therefore used to make prisms for dispersion of spectra. If some of the atoms are covalently bonded into complex ions, the infra-red and Raman spectra of these ions will be similar in solids, liquids, and solutions. The similarity of spectra is good evidence for the persistence of complex ions during phase changes. Additional spectral lines may be found if the solid contains ions which form asymmetrical hydrogen-bonds. For example, KH_2PO_4 and KH_2AsO_4 give bands at 110–130 microns wavelength, in the far infra-red, which are assigned to the frequency of protons jumping from one potential minimum to another (Fig. 4.11). Similar spectra are given by aqueous solutions containing these complex anions. Far infra-red and microwave spectra are more characteristic of complex ions with some freedom to rotate or

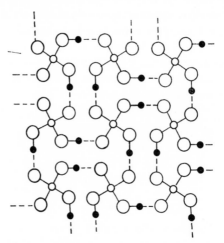

Fig. 4.11. Structure of KH_2PO_4 projected on the basal plane, with K^+ ions omitted (after Wells, 1962). $\circ = O$, $\circ = P$, $\bullet = H$, ——— $= covalent$ bond, – – – $= H$-bond. N.B. The hydrogen atoms are only fixed in the low temperature ferroelectric form of this salt: in the high temperature form they oscillate between two positions on the H-bond.

oscillate, since rotational energies lie in this region; simple ions do not absorb here.

Thermal conductivity

Ionic solids have a fair thermal conductivity, as illustrated by the data in Table 5.3. They conduct heat better than molecular solids, but one or two orders of magnitude less well than diamond or metals. As described in chapter 6, impurities and lattice defects lower the thermal conductivity by interfering with the propagation of lattice vibrations.

Electrical conductivity

At low temperatures ionic solids are insulators, but above a transition temperature, which is usually around 800°K, the electrical conductivity becomes appreciable and then increases with temperature by a factor proportional to $e^{-1/T}$. In nearly all ionic solids at high temperatures, the electricity is carried by ions and not by electrons, so that electrolytic separation of anions and cations takes place. Thus, if a potential difference is applied to a crystal of sodium chloride jus below its melting point (1088°K), sodium is deposited at the cathode and chlorine is set free at the anode as the current passes. The ions are believed to move via crystal defects, and most of the current is carried by the smaller ion, which is usually the cation. Moving an ion through a crystal requires activation energies of 1–2 eV, which explains why ionic solids only conduct when strongly heated.

Anomalously high electrical conductivities are found in the high temperature forms of a small number of ionic solids related to silver iodide, which have low lattice energies. These solids include the iodides, sulphides, selenides, and tellurides of copper (I) and silver, Cu_2HgI_4 and Ag_2HgI_4. In the high temperature form of silver iodide, which is stable between the transition point at 419°K and the melting point at 828°K, the silver ions appear to be quite free to move through the lattice of iodide ions, rather as electrons are free to move through metals. At 419°K the conductivity of silver iodide is $1 \cdot 3$ ohm^{-1} cm^{-1}, and the solid readily undergoes self-diffusion and solid reactions such as

$$\underset{\text{solid}}{2AgI} + \underset{\text{solid}}{HgI_2} \rightarrow \underset{\text{solid}}{Ag_2HgI_4}$$

The unusually high conductivity is made use of in the three-phase dry battery, Ag:AgI:C, which has a potential difference of $0 \cdot 7$ V between its electrodes.

Ferroelectric and related properties

The electric dipole moment of a crystal depends on the symmetry of the unit cell, and is only non-zero for ten of the thirty-two natural symmetry groups (Känzig, 1957). If the dipole moment of the unit cell is not zero, the resulting solid is polar, and has both piezoelectric and pyroelectric properties. A small number of polar solids are also *ferroelectric*. Ferroelectricity implies that opposite faces of a crystal spontaneously acquire an electric charge, which can be reversed by application of a suitable electric field. The dielectric constants of ferroelectric solids lie in the range 10^3–10^4, and they have some importance in electronics.

Ferroelectricity arises when asymmetrical complex ions are suitably oriented in a solid. A hypothetical two-dimensional case is illustrated in Fig. 4.12. In ferroelectric solids the local electrical fields orienting the ions are stronger than forces due to their thermal energies. Hence ferroelectricity is a property of the low temperature forms of solids, and the property is lost by a gradual transition above a critical temperature at which the dielectric constant has a sharp maximum.

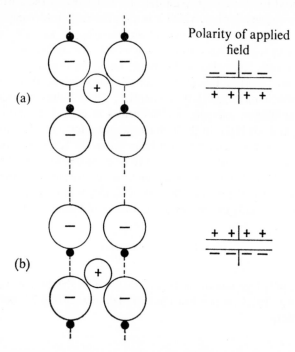

Fig. 4.12. *An imaginary two-dimensional arrangement of ions which would give rise to ferroelectricity, shown in applied fields of opposite polarity:* $\oplus$ = *cation,* $\ominus$ = *anion,* $\bullet$ = *proton,* ---- = *H-bond.*

The ferroelectric solids discovered so far are of two kinds; those containing hydrogen-bonded anions, such as KH_2PO_4 or $Ag_2H_3IO_6$, and mixed oxides, such as $PbTiO_3$. In the case of KH_2PO_4 the asymmetrical ions are $O_2P(OH)_2^-$, and these are oriented so that their positive ends are all pointed the same way (Fig. 4.11). Hence the crystal has only one ferroelectric axis. The critical temperature above which ferroelectricity is lost by thermal agitation is 122°K; it is 213°K for the deuterium analogue KD_2PO_4. In the case of $PbTiO_3$ and the technically important $BaTiO_3$, the low temperature ferroelectric forms have unit cells of lower symmetries than the high temperature forms (Fig. 4.13). This type of ferroelectric often has several different ferroelectric forms, each with a transition point, and most forms have two ferroelectric axes.

Ferroelectric solids have many analogies with ferromagnetic solids; for example they can be charged and discharged by applying suitable fields. During this process there is an irreversible absorption of energy, and the crystal is said to show hysteresis. In order to explain hysteresis

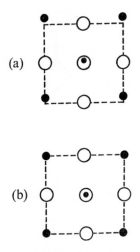

Fig. 4.13. Projection of unit cells of two forms of $PbTiO_3$: (a) low temperature, ferroelectric form; (b) high temperature, normal form: $\cdot = Ti^{4+}$, $\bullet = Pb^{2+}$, $\circ = O^{2-}$ (after Shull and Wollan, 1956).

and other phenomena, it is assumed that real crystals are made up of very many spontaneously polarized domains, but that the domains are randomly oriented. Application of an electric field causes favourably oriented domains to grow at the expense of the remainder, so that all domains are similarly oriented and the crystal remains charged when the field is removed (Fig. 4.14).

Antiferroelectric solids contain arrays of spontaneously polarized ions with neighbouring arrays polarized in the opposite sense (Fig. 4.15). They lose their antiferroelectric properties by a gradual transition on raising the temperature, and at present are only of academic interest. WO_3 and $PbZrO_3$ are known to be antiferroelectric, but the property is probably fairly common.

(a) disordered

(b) field applied

(c) ordered

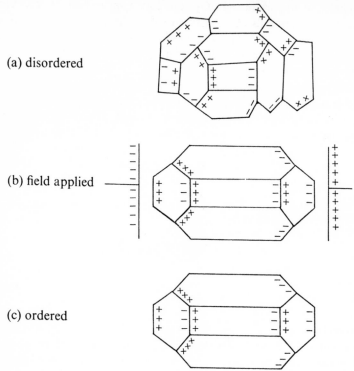

Fig. 4.14. Domain structure in a ferroelectric solid (diagrammatic).

Magnetic properties

Most ionic solids are diamagnetic. Crystals containing radical ions such as $O_2 \cdot^+$, $O_2 \cdot^-$, $NO_2 \cdot^-$, $\cdot N(OBF_3)_2^-$, or $\cdot ON(SO_3)_2^{--}$, and some of the transition metal, lanthanide, and actinide ions are paramagnetic. The number of unpaired electrons per ion can be deduced from measurements of the magnetic moment per gram of solid. These magnetic properties are not specific to solids and are usually unchanged on melting or dissolution.

In a few metal or mixed metal oxides, such as CrO_2, $CoMnO_3$, $NiMnO_3$, and ferrites MFe_2O_4, where M is a divalent metal or mixture of divalent metals, the crystals have a permanent magnetic moment at low temperatures. These solids, which are insulators, are called *ferrimagnets* to distinguish them from the metallic *ferromagnets* described in chapter 5. In ferrimagnetic solids the magnetic moments of the unpaired electrons from two or more ions are oriented anti-

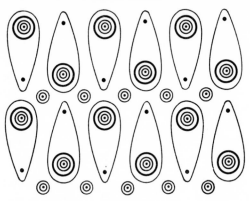

Fig. 4.15. An imaginary two-dimensional array of ions that would give rise to antiferroelectricity:

⊚ = cation, = dipolar anion.

parallel by exchange forces. This gives a resultant permanent magnetic moment to the crystal, provided the moments of the two ions are not identical. Ferrimagnetism is a low temperature phenomenon, which is lost above a transition temperature characteristic of the particular solid, and is never found in liquids or gases. Ferrimagnetic solids may be recognized by their high magnetic susceptibility, low electrical conductivity, and by the fact that they scatter thermal neutrons in a special way. Ferrimagnets have a domain structure like the ferro-electrics discussed above; the domain structure can sometimes be observed by spreading very fine iron filings on the polished surface of a crystal. They can be magnetized and demagnetized, with losses of energy due to hysteresis, by applying a suitable magnetic field. Ferri-magnets are technically important for making transformer cores, since as they are insulators no energy is lost inside them in producing eddy currents. The oldest known compass needle, lodestone, is a ferrimagnet.

Antiferromagnetic solids have the magnetic moments of their unpaired electrons oriented so that there is no resultant magnetic moment. This magnetic order is lost above the critical, or Néel, temperature, which is a gradual transition at which the magnetic susceptibility is a maximum (Fig. 5.9). The low temperature forms give extra lines in their neutron scattering pattern which vanish above the Néel temperature. A large number of transition metal salts are antiferromagnetic, e.g., Cr_2O_3, MnO, FeO, CoO, NiO, and FeF_2.

Inclusion compounds

A number of ionic solids which only exist in the solid state are of this type. They all contain gaps or channels in their lattices, and these may entrap molecules of the appropriate size and shape. The inclusion compounds formed could be stoicheiometric, but in practice they seldom are. The following types may be distinguished:

1. Solids consisting of finite ions forming clathrate compounds with small molecules, e.g., $N(C_4H_9)_4Cl \cdot xH_2O$.

2. Solids containing large spherical cage anions with small molecules or ions trapped inside, e.g., Scapolites, such as $Ca_4Al_6Si_6O_{24}$, and Ultramarine, $Na_8Al_6Si_6O_{24}S_2$.

3. Solids containing infinite linear ions which pack leaving channels between them, e.g., $(C_2H_5)_4N \cdot PO_3$ (Fig. 4.16) and $K \cdot HgNSO_3$, which take up a number of organic liquids.

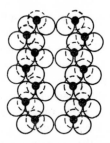

Fig. 4.16. Arrangement of $(PO_3^-)_\infty$ chains in $NaPO_3$ and Et_4NPO_3, with cations omitted. ● = P, ○ = O.

4. Solids containing infinite layer ions, which can trap ions of opposite sign between the layers, e.g., micas, clay minerals, and other complex silicates.

5. Solids containing infinite three-dimensional ions, with linear, globular, or spiral channels, e.g., zeolites and related silicates, which can function as molecular sieves.

5. Metals

The word 'metal' has a number of meanings, and this fact can give rise to ambiguities. For example, the properties of metal ions, metal atoms, and solid metals are very different, though in textbooks these are all referred to as metals. Here we shall be largely concerned with solid metals. Another ambiguity arises from applying the adjectives 'strong' and 'weak' to metals. A metal with a high electrode potential is said to be strong, while a metal with a low electrode potential is said to be weak. Hence we have the paradox that the mechanically weak solid sodium is a 'strong' metal, while the extremely tough metal tungsten is 'weak'.

A solid metal consists of an ordered array of metallic cations held together by a fluid pool of valency electrons. The valency electrons are free to move through the solid, but are by no means completely free, since their motion is restricted by the periodic electric field of the lattice of cations, and it needs a lot of energy to expel an electron from a metallic surface. All the unusual properties of metals can be qualitatively interpreted from this simple model. The quantitative treatment requires a deeper physical understanding and considerable mathematical complexity.

Many of the physical properties of metals depend markedly on the number of valency electrons per atom. Such properties include melting point, density, heat of sublimation, hardness, and malleability, as shown by the data in Table 5.1, for four metals of similar atomic weight from the first long period. Clearly both the binding energies, which determine the melting point, heat of sublimation, and hardness, and the interatomic distances, which determine the

Table 5.1

Some properties of metals compared with the number of valency electrons per atom

Metal	m.p.°K	Heat of sublimation kcals mole^{-1}	Density g cm^{-3}	No. of valency electrons/atom	Hardness
K	335	20	0·86	1	soft
Ca	1083	95	1·55	2	moderate
Sc	1473		2·5	3	hard
Ti	1893	112	4·5	4	hard

density, are related to the number of valency electrons available for binding the atoms together in the solid. The density is a function of the cationic radii.

Anomalously low melting points are found in the B metals gallium and mercury. These both have unusual crystal structures, and it is thought that not all the valency electrons are used for metallic bonding in these two solids. Some covalent metal-metal bonding may be involved, as is almost certainly the case in solid antimony and bismuth.

Anomalously low densities are found in indium, thallium, tin, and lead which are also B metals. These properties are associated with softness and malleability. X-ray studies confirm that the interatomic distances are unusually large in these metals. It is assumed that the cations concerned each have an inert pair of s-electrons, so that the number of valency electrons per atom is two less than the group valency, i.e., the cations present are thought to be In$^+$, Tl$^+$, Sn^{++}, and Pb^{++}.

Thermoelectric emission

The existence of free electrons in solid metals can be inferred from many of their properties, among which *thermoelectric emission* is a fairly convincing demonstration of their presence. On heating any metal sufficiently hot, it emits electrons. The temperature required depends on the *work function*, which is the energy needed to remove an electron from the surface of the metal, and is equal to the ionization energy of the gaseous metal atoms less any kinetic energy possessed by the electrons in the solid. Since work functions for most metals exceed 4 eV, the temperatures needed are around 2000°K, and many metals vaporize before they show the thermoelectric effect. However, refractory metals, such as tungsten which has a work function of

4·5 eV, begin to emit electrons below their melting points. The current emitted per unit area of metal surface is proportional to $T^2 e^{-E/kT}$ where E is the work function and k is Boltzmann's constant. For technical applications of electron emission, the work function can be reduced by making the metal a cathode with a negative potential of many kilovolts.

Structures of metals

Most metals have their atoms close-packed with a co-ordination number of 12. About one-third have the body-centred cubic structure

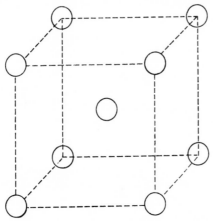

Fig. 5.1. The body-centred cubic unit cell.

which has a co-ordination number of 8, and these have lower densities than the forms with close-packed structures. Examples of the three commonest types of packing are:

Cubic close-packed (Fig. 2.1): Ag, Au, Ca, Co, Cu, Fe, Ir, La, Ni, Pb, Pd, Pt, Rh, Sc, Sr, and Tl.

Hexagonal close-packed (Fig. 2.2): Be, Ca, Co, Hf, La-Lu, Mg, Mo, Ni, Os, Re, Ru, Sc, Tc, Ti, Tl, Y, and Zr.

Body-centred cubic (Fig. 5.1): Ba, Cr, Cs, Fe, Hf, K, Li, Mo, Na Nb, Rb, Ta, Ti, U, V, W, and Zr.

Other metals, including Bi, Cd, Ga, Hg, In, Mn, Sb, Sn, U, W, and Zr have anomalous structures, many of which are distorted variants of one of the close-packed structures. It should be clear from the fact that several elements occur in more than one of these lists that polymorphism is quite common among metals.

Mechanical properties of metals

The hardness of metals is determined to a large extent by the lattice energy, which in turn is determined by the valency. For example, sodium, with only one valency electron per atom for bonding, is extremely soft, while tungsten, with perhaps six valency electrons per atom, is very hard. Great hardness is frequently associated with brittleness. When subjected to impact or great stress, tungsten wire will snap, giving an irregular surface quite unlike the cleavage planes of ionic crystals. On the other hand, many metals, such as sodium, have considerable malleability, that is, they bend without breaking. This property is found only in crystalline metals and some amorphous solids. In metals it is a consequence of the lack of directional forces between atoms, since the valency electrons are not confined in oriented, finite orbitals. Malleability is greatest for cubic close-packed metals, and especially for those with few valency electrons per atom, e.g., Ag, Au, Cu, K, Na, Pb, and β-Tl. The ductility of metals, which is their capacity for being drawn out into thin wires, is greatest for hexagonal close-packed crystals such as Cd and Zn.

If the lattice energy of a metal is known, its theoretical strength can be calculated. The actual strengths are found to be a very small fraction, usually one per cent or less, of the theoretical strengths. The reason for this discrepancy lies in the fact that nearly all real crystals are full of imperfections and defects, as described in chapter 6, and tend to break along lines of weakness. Defects can be generated by repeated bending or 'cold working'. which causes the hardening and ultimate breakage of most metals. Nearly perfect crystals, or 'whiskers', of pure metals may be hundreds of times stronger than ordinary defective crystals, and are now of considerable technical importance.

Alloys

An *alloy* is a substance with metallic properties containing two or more elements, at least one of which is a metal. Of the many alloys known, the majority are non-stoicheiometric. Some—like brass, steel, and dural—are of enormous technical importance. It is difficult to generalize about such a vast subject, but Hume-Rothery has given two useful rules concerning alloys:

1. Two metals will not dissolve appreciably in one another if their atomic radii differ by more than 15 per cent, e.g. Cu (radius 1·28 Å) will alloy with Zn (radius 1·37 Å), but not with Pb (radius

1·75 Å). The main exceptions to this rule involve the interstitial compounds of some metals with hydrogen, carbon, boron, and nitrogen, which are discussed below.

2. Corresponding phases of similar alloys have similar numbers of valency electrons per atom, as shown in Table 5.2. In practice, these numbers may not be precisely defined, as most alloys are non-stoicheiometric. This rule is also ambiguous for metals with variable valency, such as transition metals. For example, it must be assumed that the cobalt atoms in body-centred cubic CoAl contribute no valency electrons to the bonding for this rule to apply.

Table 5.2

Structures of intermediate phases and the number of valency electrons per atom

Phase	Structure	No. of valency electrons/atom	Examples
α	Face-centred cubic	1·36–1·42	$Cu + \leqslant 20\%$ Al
β	Body-centred cubic or cubic close-packed	1·50	$CuZn$, Cu_3Al, Cu_5Sn
γ	Complex	1·58–1·67	Cu_5Zn_8, Cu_9Al_4, $Cu_{31}Sn_8$
ϵ	Hexagonal close-packed	1·75	$CuZn_3$, Cu_3Sn

The theory of alloys is insufficiently advanced to predict the structures of complex binary or tertiary alloys. In the case of alloys of formula MM′, the following empirical generalizations can be made:

If M is an alkali or alkaline earth metal, and M′ a metal from Group IIB or IIIB, the alloy MM′ will have either a CsCl (Fig. 4.2) or a NaTl structure (Fig. 5.2).

If M is a transition metal (including Group IB), and M′ is an element from Group IVB, VB, or VIB, the compound MM′ usually has the NiAs structure (Fig. 5.3).

Alloys may be *ordered* or *disordered*. Taking brass, CuZn, as a simple example, this means that the copper atoms may either alternate with zinc atoms throughout the lattice, or all the atoms may be arranged at random (Fig. 1.14). Theoretically, all alloys should be perfectly ordered at absolute zero, but in practice disordered alloys can be supercooled below their transition temperatures. If an ordered alloy is warmed up from a low temperature, disorder sets in at a critical point as a gradual transition, and can be detected by changes in the specific heat, electrical conductivity, or X-ray scattering pattern.

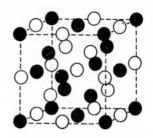

Fig. 5.2. The NaTl unit crystal cell: ● = Na, ○ = Tl.

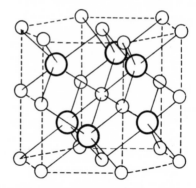

Fig. 5.3. The NiAs unit crystal cell: ○ = Ni, ○ = As.

Metallic interstitial compounds

The hydrides, borides, carbides, and nitrides (and probably also some beryllides and silicides) of metals in Groups IIIA–VIA have metallic properties. They are opaque, with metallic lustre, are mostly paramagnetic and have high electrical conductivities which decrease with a rise in temperature. They also have extremely high lattice energies, and include some of the hardest and most refractory solids known, such as tungsten carbide. Some examples have been listed in Table 1.2.

These substances resemble alloys rather than ionic or covalent solids, not only in being non-stoicheiometric, but also in not obeying normal valency rules. For example, V_2C ranges in composition from $VC_{0.37}$ to $VC_{0.5}$, and does not contain divalent vanadium. Again, while TiC could be a covalent solid like SiC, most other compounds in this category have formulae which imply that they are electron-deficient according to classical valency theory, e.g., ZrB, TaN, W_2C, and Pd_2H. Although their structures often differ from those of the parent metals, these solids are best visualized as close-packed metal lattices containing small atoms of H, B, C, or N in their interstices. It appears that all the compounds of formula MX contain cubic close-packed M atoms, while those with formula M_2X contain hexagonal close-packed M atoms. The high density, and other properties mentioned above, are consistent with this conception of interstitial packing. Because of their remarkable strength, hardness, or refractory nature, many interstitial solids have some technical importance, e.g., TaC for high temperature crucibles, WC for machine tools and for high pressure devices. Chemically they are inert.

Dissolution of metals

Despite the alloying restrictions mentioned above, most metals have at least a measurable solubility in other liquid metals. Thus mercury forms amalgams with most metals, but only those with similar atomic radii dissolve freely. This type of solution has a few uses in analysis and also in metal extraction. For example, native silver and the platinum metals can be extracted from suitable minerals by treatment with molten lead. The silver can be further extracted from molten lead by agitation with the practically immiscible molten zinc, which is the basis for the Parkes process.

Metals are mostly chemically reactive, and dissolve irreversibly in many solvents other than liquid metals. Thus water, hydrochloric and other acids, and most oxidizing agents can be reduced by treatment with suitable metals. The reducing powers of metals are a natural consequence of their being a source of electrons. The reducing power of a metal is measured by its *electrode potential*, but the observed rate of reduction may be influenced by the formation of oxide layers on the metallic surface. The electrode potentials of some metals and their reducing powers are compared in Fig. 5.4. Metals with an electrode potential below that of hydrogen will not reduce hydrochloric acid to hydrogen, and are said to be *noble*.

Optical properties of metals

The physical theory of metals involves the mathematical treatment of the motion of electrons in an infinite electric field which is periodic in three dimensions. In order to treat large numbers of electrons it is

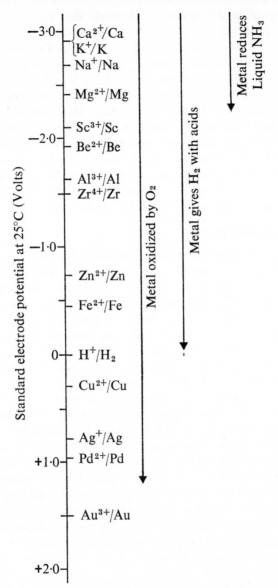

Fig. 5.4. Comparison of standard electrode potentials and reducing power of metals.

necessary to use Fermi-Dirac statistics, which take account of the
discrete energy levels required by the quantum theory, and also the
fact that only two electrons can occupy any given level (the Pauli
principle); Boltzmann statistics, which are used for molecules in the
kinetic theory of gases, give incorrect results for electrons. The
solutions of the equations lead to the concept that electrons in
metals occupy restricted energy ranges or *bands*. The *allowed energy
bands* correspond to the s, p, d, f... energy levels of an electron bound
to a free atom, but they are much broader, while the *forbidden energy
gaps* separating the bands are much narrower than in the free atom,
and are often zero (Fig. 5.5).

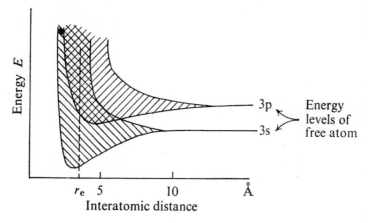

Fig. 5.5. *Some energy bands of metallic sodium, showing overlap at the
equilibrium interatomic distance* r_e.

The energy bands occupied by electrons in metals can be studied
experimentally by bombarding metal targets with hard ultra-violet
radiation or soft X-rays of known energy. It is found that electrons
are emitted over certain energy ranges corresponding to the allowed
energy bands in the metal. The expulsion of electrons by energetic
radiation is called photoelectric emission, and is important in the
electronics industry. The minimum energy of radiation needed to
cause photoelectric emission measures the work function of the
metal. The work functions of three metals are shown in Fig. 5.6.
Caesium and tungsten have unusually small work functions, and
emit electrons when exposed to ultra-violet light, but most other
metals have to be irradiated with X-rays before they will emit.

Thin films of metals are transparent over a range of energies in the ultra-violet region where electrons are not emitted, e.g., caesium is transparent at wavelengths shorter than 4400 Å in the visible region. Otherwise, all metals are opaque and totally reflecting in the visible, infra-red, and microwave regions. This reflectivity is of great technical importance, e.g., in mirrors, heat reflectors, and radar wave-guides, as well as giving rise to the lustre so characteristic of metals. At these energies the electrons move through the metal fast enough to intercept and scatter any photon of radiation which strikes the metal surface, so that one is effectively 'seeing' electrons. In addition to their

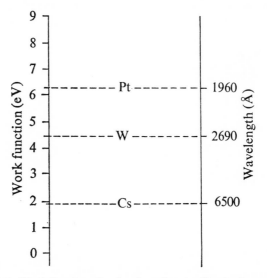

Fig. 5.6. Work functions for the photoelectric effect in three metals.

reflective powers, metals may have absorption spectra due to electronic transitions in or near the visible region. Thus copper and gold are coloured because the energy of the electronic transition between the sp- and d-bands happens to be in the visible region. In the case of copper, the d-band is 2·3 eV below the sp-band, and electrons are excited from the d-band by green light; in the case of silver, this excitation requires ultra-violet light, while in the alkali metals the corresponding absorption band is in the infra-red region. Absorption spectra of metals may be obtained by using very thin specimens. For example, gold leaf which has been etched to a thickness of about 100 Å by floating it on potassium cyanide solution looks green in transmitted light. Metals do not have rotation spectra, and their vibration spectra which should occur in the far infra-red region are little known.

Thermal conduction

At room temperatures, metals have thermal conductivities which are several orders of magnitude higher than those of most other solids, apart from diamond, as shown by the data in Table 5.3. The valency electrons carry most of the heat, except in impure metals and disordered alloys, where lattice vibrations may carry up to 50 per cent of the heat. Lattice defects and impurity atoms disturb the periodicity of the electric field in which the electrons move, and therefore scatter electrons from their normally straight paths. It is not surprising that thermal conductivities are rather sensitive to these crystal imperfections. Since thermal conductivity is inversely proportional to atomic weight, light elements are the best conductors of heat.

Table 5.3

Thermal conductivities of various solids, at 273°K unless otherwise stated

Substance	Class	Thermal cond. $(cal\ sec^{-1}cm^{-1}deg^{-1})$
Argon, Ar	Molecular solid	0·00029 (90°K)
Ice, H_2O	,, ,,	0·0053
Diamond, C	Covalent solid	1·6
Graphite, C	,, ,,	0·037
Quartz, SiO_2	,, ,,	0·017–0·033 (anisotropic)
Sodium chloride, NaCl	Ionic solid	0·022
Rubidium iodide, RbI	,, ,,	0·0078
Silver, Ag	Metal	1·06
Aluminium, Al	,,	0·54
Copper, Cu	,,	0·73
Sodium, Na	,,	0·33
Silicon, Si	Semiconductor	0·20
Germanium, Ge	,,	0·14

The heat capacities of metals at NTP are due largely to the metallic cations, with very little contribution from the electrons. This agrees with predictions from Fermi-Dirac statistics, and the observed specific heats of metals provide good evidence that electrons do not obey Boltzmann statistics.

Electrical conduction

Metals are characterized by their high electrical conductivities. Their resistivities at 273°K range from $1 \cdot 5 \times 10^{-6}$ ohm cm for silver to

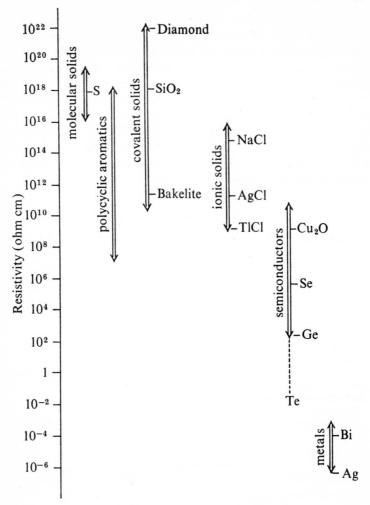

Fig. 5.7. Electrical resistivities of materials at NTP.

$7 \cdot 1 \times 10^{-4}$ ohm cm for α-manganese, which is six orders of magnitude lower than all other simple solids except graphite and tellurium (Fig. 5.7). In addition, the conductivity decreases with rising temperature, which again is characteristic of metals, and also of graphite.

The high electrical conductivity is easily accounted for by the freedom with which electrons can move in a metal. In theory, a perfect lattice of identical stationary cations should be transparent to electrons, so that a pure metal should be a perfect conductor with no electrical resistance. This perfect conduction has been observed in many metals and metallic interstitial compounds at very low temperatures, and is called *superconduction*. Superconduction

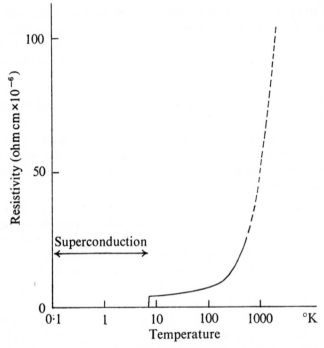

Fig. 5.8. Variation of resistivity of niobium with temperature, showing superconduction below 8·9°K.

implies that metals are transparent to radiation of low frequency, such as a.c. at 50 cycles sec^{-1}, though they reflect higher frequency microwave radiation.

Superconductors have an electrical resistance of less than 10^{-17} times the resistance at 273°K, and so have many potential applications. Most of the metallic elements only become superconducting below 5°K, but lead and some metallic interstitial compounds and alloys have higher transition temperatures, e.g., Pb 7·2°K; NbC 10·1°K; MoN 12°K; Nb_3Sn 18°K (Fig. 5.8). Superconduction has not been found in the alkali metals, though there is no theoretical reason why they should not show it. It has not been found in ferromagnetic metals such as iron either, which is not surprising since large magnetic fields are known to lower the transition temperature or inhibit super-conduction altogether. The theory of superconduction is not yet able to explain some of these facts and other observations, e.g., the drop in thermal conductivity which occurs when metals become super-conductors.

At all but the lowest temperatures, metals have a resistance to the passage of electricity, which arises from collisions between electrons and metal atoms in the lattice; the conduction electrons are thereby scattered. There are several independent causes of electrical resistance in metals, all of which increase with rising temperature, i.e.:

1. Vibrations of metal atoms, which destroy the instantaneous periodicity of the lattice.

2. Lattice defects of all kinds. These may be increased in number not only by heating but also by cold-working the metal. For example, cold-worked copper has a greater resistivity than a fresh crystal of copper.

3. Impurities, disorder, and other imperfections which interfere with the regular periodicity of the lattice. Impurities always increase the internal scattering of electrons and hence the electrical resistance, which explains why electrical transmission lines are made of very pure copper or aluminium. Disordered alloys such as brass have a much greater resistivity than the ordered forms. Metals with complex, distorted structures such as bismuth and manganese have a much greater resistivity than metals with cubic symmetry.

According to the energy band theory, the difference between electrical conductors and insulators is the width of the forbidden energy band E. The number of electrons in the highest allowed band is of the order of 10^{21}–10^{23} electrons per mole for metals, where E is usually zero or less than 0·01 eV. If E is zero, the upper bands are said to overlap (Fig. 5.5). For example, the alkali metals have wide, half-filled s-bands overlapping narrower, empty p-bands; and copper, silver, and gold have similar bands together with overlapping d-bands. The alkaline earth metals have less overlap between the filled s-band and the empty p-bands. In the transition metals of the first long period, the electrons of the 4s-band carry most of the current, but the resistivity is relatively high because of frequent transitions to the 3d-band, which readily captures moving electrons.

Magnetic properties

At room temperature, different metals display all known types of magnetic properties. Thus beryllium and the metals of Groups IB–VIB are all diamagnetic, while nearly all the A metals are paramagnetic. Ferromagnetism and antiferromagnetism are only found in metals with unfilled d- or f-bands. Iron, cobalt, nickel, dysprosium, gadolinium, and a number of alloys (e.g., MnAs, CrTe, and Cu_2MnAl) and interstitial compounds (e.g., MnB, Mn_4N) have ferromagnetic forms, while α-manganese, chromium, and a few alloys (e.g., MnSe, CrSb) are antiferromagnetic at low temperatures.

The magnetic properties of solids, apart from their diamagnetism, depend markedly on temperature. Figure 5.9 illustrates the dependence of magnetic susceptibility on temperature for the four types of magnetic solids. The susceptibility is independent of temperature for diamagnetic solids, and proportional to T^{-1} for paramagnetic solids. Both ferromagnetism and antiferromagnetism are lost above a transition temperature, known as the Curie temperature and Néel temperature respectively. Iron has a Curie temperature of 1043°K, while several of the lanthanide metals have Curie temperatures below 273°K and are ferromagnetic only at low temperatures. Although these magnetic properties can be understood qualitatively, it is not possible to predict the magnetic behaviour of unknown alloys, nor to make quantitative estimates of Curie temperatures from current hypotheses. Theory predicts that all metals, except perhaps iron, cobalt, and nickel, should become diamagnetic at absolute zero.

The magnetic moments or spins of the electrons are all paired in diamagnetic metals, so that there is no net electron magnetism. In paramagnetic metals one or more electrons per atom have unpaired magnetic moments, but these moments are oriented at random in the solid lattice. Ferromagnetic metals contain unpaired electrons whose magnetic moments are oriented so as to reinforce one another. The orientation energy is opposed by the thermal energy of the electrons, and the two energies are equal at the Curie temperature. There is still some disagreement among physicists as to the nature of the orientation energy. It may be an energy of exchange of electrons between adjacent atoms, or it may involve an interaction between electrons in outer s-bands and either d-bands in transition metals or f-bands in

7

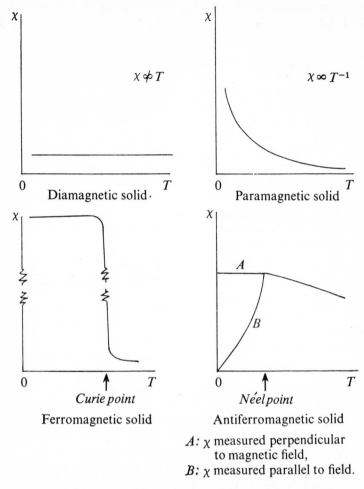

Fig. 5.9. Variation of magnetic susceptibility χ with temperature.

lanthanides. The interatomic distances may be important in determining whether the exchange energy is positive or negative. According to one current theory, transition metals are most likely to be ferromagnetic if the interatomic radius greatly exceeds twice the mean radius of the outer d-shell. However, the data in Table 5.4 do not support any simple correlation between interatomic distances and magnetic behaviour, and no theory correctly predicts the magnetic properties of solid transition metals.

Table 5.4

Interatomic distances and ferromagnetism in transition metals

Metal	Magnetic properties	No. of 3d electrons	r_{M-M} (Å)	$r_{3d \, shell}$	$r_{4s \, shell}$
V	Paramagnetic	5	2·62	0·49	1·52
Cr	Antiferromagnetic	6	2·50	0·45	1·51
Mn	,,	7	2·73	0·42	1·31
Fe	Ferromagnetic	8	2·48	0·39	1·22
Co	,,	9	2·51	0·36	1·14
Ni	,,	10	2·49	0·34	1·07
Cu	Diamagnetic	10	2·56	0·32	1·03

Note: the interatomic distances were obtained from X-ray diffraction work (Wells, 1962), and the radii of the electron shells are approximate, calculated values (Phillips and Williams, 1965).

Antiferromagnetic metals contain unpaired electrons whose magnetic moments are oriented in such a way as to oppose one another in the solid lattice. The best known are chromium and manganese, with Néel temperatures of 475 and 100°K respectively. At present, antiferromagnetism has none of the great technical importance associated with ferromagnetism.

Perfect crystals of ferromagnetic solids are spontaneously magnetized, but most real crystals are made up of a mosaic of randomly oriented microcrystals or domains, so that the spontaneous magnetization of the domains can only be revealed by microscopic observations of polished specimens which have been sprinkled with iron filings. Energy is needed to re-orient these domains, which may be obtained by applying a magnetic field. The process of orientation is thermodynamically irreversible, so that the magnetization of iron bars shows hysteresis. It gives rise to permanent magnets with many applications.

Two unique properties of ferromagnetic and antiferromagnetic metals should be mentioned here:

1. If placed in a strong magnetic field, the metals absorb microwave radiation at energies corresponding to the precessional energies of their electron spins.

2. The metals scatter neutrons, which also have a magnetic moment, in a manner which differs qualitatively from scattering by atoms (Fig. 5.10).

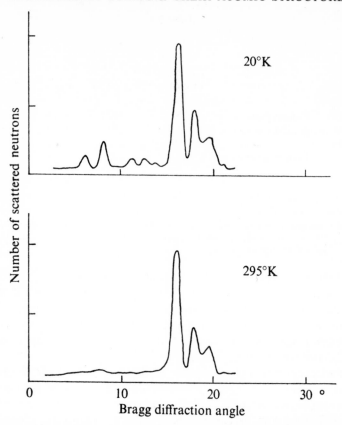

Fig. 5.10. Scattering of slow neutrons by α-Mn above and below the Néel temperature. The extra peaks at the lower temperature are caused by antiferromagnetism.

Catalysis by solid metals

Metallic catalysis is not well understood theoretically, and is still as much an art as a science, despite its industrial importance. It is essentially a property of metal surfaces, so that finely divided metals such as platinum black and Raney nickel (made by dissolving the aluminium from a nickel–aluminium alloy with potassium hydroxide) are much better catalysts than the massive metals. A *catalyst* is a substance which increases the rate of a chemical reaction, without itself undergoing a change in the overall reaction. Metallic surfaces function as catalysts by absorbing thin layers of molecules, which may then react together at a lower temperature than they would in the gas phase, because the activation energy is smaller for the reaction on the surface. Thus a platinum wire placed in an unlit Bunsen will absorb molecules of gas and oxygen which react on its surface; the surface soon gets red hot and ignites the gas. All catalytic surfaces are liable to be poisoned by traces of impurities, such as sulphur or arsenic, which are strongly adsorbed and prevent the desired reaction from taking place.

The adsorption of gas molecules on metal surfaces may take place by weak Van der Waals or 'physical' forces, or by strong chemical bonding, but between these two extremes there is a continuous range of interaction energies. Thus the inert gases are physically adsorbed by metals at low temperatures, but the energy of bonding is so small that they are driven off by heating to room temperature. On the other hand, gaseous oxygen, fluorine, and chlorine have a great affinity for electrons and are strongly adsorbed by nearly all metal surfaces, forming ionic or more or less covalent bonds, which are often not broken by heating *in vacuo* to the melting point of the metal. Gold is unique in *not* adsorbing oxygen on to its surface. A few other gas molecules, such as N_2 and N_2O, have a weak affinity for electrons but are adsorbed by most of the transition metals. They usually increase the magnetic susceptibility of the metal surfce. Alternatively, electron-donor molecules, such as H_2, H_2O, NH_3, CO, and hydrocarbons, tend to decrease the magnetic susceptibility and also the electrical conductivity of metallic surfaces on which they are adsorbed. They are taken up mainly by transition metals, and it is possible that they donate electrons to unfilled d-bands.

The complexity of factors involved in choosing a catalyst now becomes apparent. If it is desired to react together two electron-donor molecules, such as ethylene and hydrogen, almost any transition metal should be a suitable catalyst, but some may have surfaces which are geometrically more favourable than others. In practice, the maximum rate of reaction is found for metals which have a lattice spacing of 3·75 Å. Rhodium is the best catalyst, nickel, palladium, and platinum are all good, while tantalum and tungsten are poor (Fig. 5.11). Scale models can be used to show that this lattice spacing allows the ethylene and hydrogen molecules to sit on the surface in a manner conducive to their reacting together to form ethane. Electronic factors are also important, as is shown by the observation that the rate of catalysis by nickel decreases greatly as increasing amounts of copper are alloyed with the nickel, though the lattice spacing is scarcely altered.

If, however, the desired reaction is between an electron donor and an electron acceptor molecule, there are no general rules to guide the selection of a catalyst, except that a transition metal or alloy is the

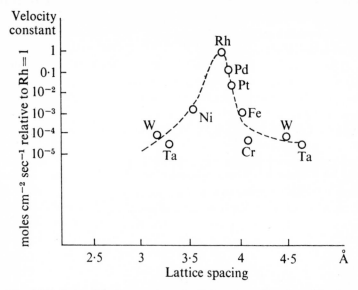

Fig. 5.11. *Rate of hydrogenation of ethylene as a function of lattice spacing in transition metals (after Trapnell, 1954).*

most likely material. For example, in the industrially important reactions

$$N_2 + 3H_2 \rightleftharpoons 2NH_3$$
$$4NH_3 + 5O_2 \rightleftharpoons 4NO + 6H_2O$$
$$2SO_2 + O_2 \rightleftharpoons 2SO_3$$

the catalysts used, which are respectively iron, platinum, and vanadium with traces of promoters added, were all discovered empirically, and the reasons for their excellence are still unknown.

6. Semiconductors and defective solids

Almost all real crystals are imperfect, and the presence of the commoner types of defect can often be inferred from a study of the macroscopic properties. It is possible to classify crystal defects fairly simply, though the experimental identification and location of particular kinds of defect may be difficult. The simplest classification is based on the dimensionality of the defect.

1. *Zero-dimensional or point defects*

These are of two types, involving either a missing atom or *Schottky defect*, or a displaced atom or *Frenkel defect* (Fig. 6.1). Both are frequent in metals, covalent and ionic solids, but not in molecular solids. They affect colour, luminescence, electrical conductivity, etc., as discussed above, and also catalytic activity. Pair and cluster defects have similar properties.

2. *One-dimensional defects*

These are subdivided into *edge* and *screw dislocations*. An edge dislocation is a row of atoms marking the edge of an extra crystallographic plane (Fig. 6.2), while a screw dislocation is a row of atoms about which a crystallographic plane spirals (Fig. 6.3). Both types are common in crystals, and are often mobile. They are important in crystal growth, as in the phenomenon of twinning, and chiefly affect the strength and mechanical properties of the solid, and sometimes also its electrical conductivity.

3. *Two-dimensional defects*

These include stacking faults in close-packed layers of atoms. They affect the mechanical properties of the solid and are less mobile than one-dimensional defects.

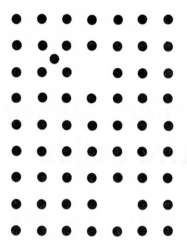

Fig. 6.1. Two-dimensional lattice showing Frenkel defect (above) and Schottky defect (below).

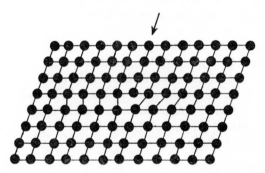

Fig. 6.2. Two-dimensional diagram of an edge dislocation.

4. *Three-dimensional defects*

All real crystals are made up of many small microcrystals or domains, each of which may be nearly perfect or possess other types of defect. The edge of each domain may vary from a few hundred Å to a few centimetres. This type of defect is important in studies of melting, polymorphic transitions, and X-ray scattering, and its effects on ferroelectric and ferromagnetic solids have already been discussed. Domain boundaries are lines of weakness along which crystals tend to break when subjected to great stress.

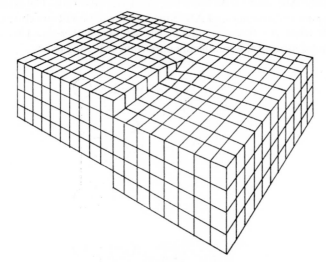

Fig. 6.3. Diagram of screw dislocation in a three-dimensional lattice (after Read, 1953).

Semiconductors

A semiconductor is a solid electronic conductor with a resistivity which is usually in the range 10^{-2} to 10^9 ohm cm at room temperature, and whose electrical conductivity increases exponentially with temperature. Solid *ionic* conductors have been discussed in chapter 4, while the rare class of molecular solids with appreciable electrical conductivity have been discussed in chapter 2. Semiconduction is a property found in many solids, which may be giant covalent molecules such as Ge and Si, or more commonly in compounds of elements from the centre of the periodic table whose constituent atoms do not differ greatly in electronegativity, e.g., GaAs and PbS. In the latter type of compound the bonds between the atoms are covalent, but are more or less polar and so may have considerable ionic character. A few semiconductors with high conductivities, such as InSb, are more closely related to metals than to ionic solids.

The structures of semiconductors show some interesting regularities if they are classified according to the number of valency electrons per electronegative atom (Hulliger and Mooser, 1965). If this number is 8, corresponding to normal covalent or ionic bonding, the structure found is either that of sphalerite or wurtzite (Fig. 6.4). For example: SiC, InN, and ZnS all have the wurtzite structure, while another form of ZnS, AlP, and GaAs have the sphalerite structure. The wurtzite structure for a compound AB reduces to the diamond structure (Fig. 1.12) when A=B, as in silicon, germanium, and α-tin. This class includes most of the technically important semiconductors.

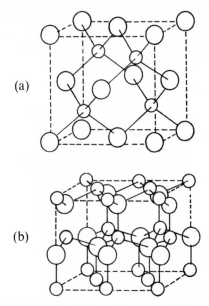

Fig. 6.4. *Unit crystal cells of* (a) *sphalerite, and* (b) *wurtzite:* ∘=*Zn*, ○ = *S*, ——— = *covalent bond.*

If the number of valency electrons per electronegative atom is 7, the electronegative atoms are covalently bonded in pairs, as in solid iodine. This happens, for example, with the antimony atoms in ZnSb, and with the sulphur atoms in FeS_2 (Fig. 6.5). The latter compound contains divalent iron.

If the number of valency electrons per electronegative atom is 6, the electronegative atoms are often found bonded into zigzag or spiral chains, as in solid grey selenium (Fig. 3.1). This structure has been found for the arsenic atoms in LiAs, the silicon atoms in CaSi, and the phosphorus atoms in ZnP_2. In a few cases, such as CoP_3, $RhAs_3$, and $IrSb_3$, the electronegative atoms form X_4 ring polymers, but no analogues of the S_8 ring polymer in solid sulphur have been discovered.

If the number of valency electrons per electronegative atom is 5, the electronegative atoms may either be arranged in tetrahedra, as in white phosphorus, or in infinite layers resembling those found in black phosphorus or solid arsenic (Fig. 1.13). Thus in the compounds NaSi, KGe, RbSn, and CsPb the 'anion' is an X_4 tetrahedral cluster, while in $CaSi_2$ the 'anion' is an infinite two-dimensional layer of silicon atoms.

If the number of valency electrons per electronegative atom is 4, the electronegative atoms may form either a diamond lattice, as in NaIn, or a graphite lattice, as in MgB_2 and $CaGa_2$ (see Fig. 1.12).

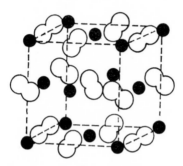

Fig. 6.5. Unit crystal cell of pyrites (FeS_2): ● $= Fe$, ⊂⊃ $= S_2$.

A few semiconductors, such as GaS, have 9 valency electrons per electronegative atom. In this case the electropositive atoms are arranged in pairs, so that this example might be written $Ga_2^{4+}[S^{2-}]_2$, though it is predominantly a covalent compound. Mercurous compounds are all of this type, but are mostly molecular solids.

Intrinsic and extrinsic semiconductors

A substance is said to be an *intrinsic semiconductor* if its resistivity is in the semiconductor range when the substance is prepared in pure, stoicheiometric crystals. The forbidden energy gap between the highest filled band and the lowest unfilled band is between 0·2 and 2·2 eV for most intrinsic semiconductors. At absolute zero all semiconductors are insulators, but as the temperature is raised some electrons are excited to the lowest unfilled band by thermal energy, and the electrical conductivity rises. The electricity is conducted partly by the excited electrons and partly by the *positive holes* left in the highest filled band after excitation. Theory shows that the number of electrons excited is proportional to $e^{-E/kT}$, where E is the energy needed to excite the electrons (i.e., the width of the forbidden energy gap). While this agrees with the experimental dependence of conductivity on temperature, the actual conductivity is determined by the mobility of electrons or positive holes in the crystal. Electron mobilities are not directly related to the energy gap, as shown in Fig. 6.6, which also illustrates the range of mobilities and energy gaps

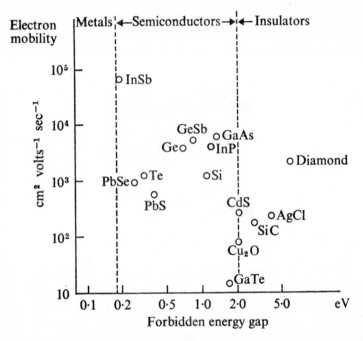

Fig. 6.6. Mobilities of electrons in semiconductors at NTP as a function of the energy gap (after Jonscher, 1965).

found in semiconductors at NTP. Examples of intrinsic semiconductors include B, Si, Ge, PbS, GaAs, InSb, and Fe_3O_4.

A number of insulators become semiconductors when they are non-stoicheiometric or when they are impure; they are called *extrinsic semiconductors.* The number of electrons in the lowest unfilled band may be increased by the presence of lattice defects and/or impurities. Examples of extrinsic semiconductors are impure Si or Ge, ZnO, TiO_2, and Mn_3O_4.

The electrical resistance of all types of semiconductor is profoundly affected by impurities, since these modify the number of electrons in the upper bands and may add extra bands. Consider the case of solid silicon. If N silicon atoms in the lattice are replaced by N phosphorus atoms, the lattice gains N electrons and a negative, or *n-type semiconductor* results. If on the other hand the silicon atoms are replaced by N boron atoms, the lattice becomes electron deficient by N electrons, and a positive or *p-type semiconductor* results. The impurity atoms are called *donors* or *acceptors* according to whether they donate or abstract electrons to or from the lattice. Although no semiconductor can be made perfectly pure, the impurity levels in silicon can be reduced to less than 1 part in 10^9, and if the impurity atoms left

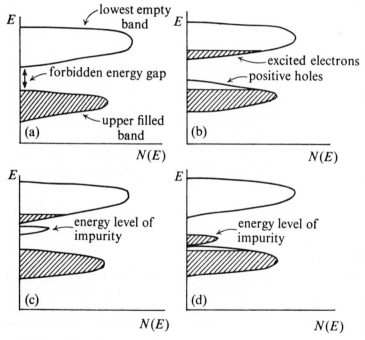

Fig. 6.7. *Energy bands in semiconductors:*

    (a) *semiconductor at low temperatures, with insulating properties;*
    (b) *semiconductor at room temperature;*
    (c) *extrinsic semiconductor with electron donor impurity (n-type);*
    (d) *extrinsic semiconductor with electron acceptor impurity (p-type);*

E = *energy*, $N(E)$ = *number of electrons with energy E. Filled energy levels are hatched.*

consist of equal numbers of donors and acceptors, their effects cancel out and the intrinsic semiconduction can be studied (Figs. 6.7 and 6.8).

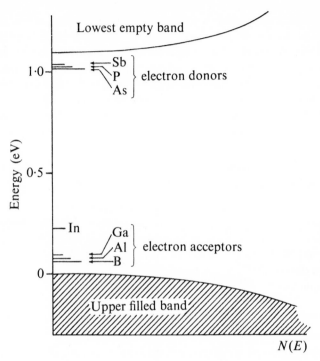

Fig. 6.8. Energy levels of some impurities in the forbidden energy gap of silicon.

Optical properties

If E is the forbidden energy gap, radiation of energy greater than E will be strongly absorbed. Table 6.1 gives values for E in eV for a number of pure, intrinsic semiconductors, together with values of the corresponding wavelength λ in microns, calculated from the relation

$$E\lambda = 1 \cdot 24.$$

It can be seen that E is usually in the infra-red region, but may be in the visible region for a few semiconductors such as GaP and SiC. Hence, a number of semiconductors are opaque in the ultra-violet, visible, and near infra-red regions. Many of them have reflecting surfaces resembling, though less striking than, the lustre of metals.

Table 6.1

Forbidden energy gaps for some pure, intrinsic semiconductors

Substance	Energy gap in eV	Wavelength in microns
B	0·9	1·4
Si	1·1	1·1
Ge	0·76	1·65
α-Sn	0·06	21
PbS	0·4	3·1
PbSe	0·5	2·5
PbTe	0·22	5·6
GaP	2·2	0·62
GaAs	1·4	0·89
InSb	0·2	6·2
SiC	2·8	0·44

Semiconductors are transparent to most radiation whose energy is less than E, that is, in the infra-red and microwave regions, though they may have absorption bands corresponding to the energies of the lattice vibrations if they are polar. These are insensitive to the presence of impurities.

Luminescence

Luminescence is the spontaneous emission of light. *Fluorescence* is prompt, and *phosphorescence* delayed luminescence following excitation. Two important generalizations about luminescence are:

1. The energy of the emitted light is usually less than the energy of excitation.
2. The half-life of phosphorescence becomes shorter as the temperature is raised.

Excitation of an electron to a high energy band, leaving a positive hole in a lower band, can lead to luminescence. The excited electron may lose its energy immediately, or after some delay, by emitting radiation. The energy may be lost in two or more steps, any of which may or may not involve the emission of a light photon.

In practice, it is found that many luminescent substances are either semiconductors or have substantial numbers of lattice defects or impurity atoms in them. Most phosphorescent substances, or *phosphors*, are semiconductors with controlled amounts of impurities added to them. Some have great industrial importance, and almost all of them have been discovered empirically. The following varieties of luminescent solid have been distinguished according to the source of excitation.

Photoluminescent solids are excited by visible or ultra-violet light. They include anthracene and other polycyclic hydrocarbons, zinc sulphide, strontium sulphide containing bismuth, and a number of substances which are used to coat the inside walls of 'fluorescent' lamps, such as impure $MgWO_4$ (containing Pb) and $ZnSiO_3$ (containing Mn).

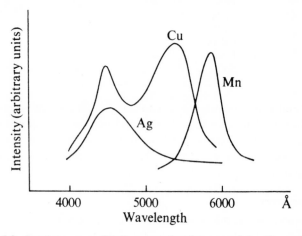

Fig. 6.9. Luminescence of ZnS activated with traces of Ag, Cu, and Mn following exposure to ultra-violet radiation (after Azaroff and Brophy, 1963).

Cathodoluminescent solids are excited by bombardment with electrons or nuclear particles such as alpha particles. The best known is zinc sulphide containing about 0·1 per cent of copper as an impurity; impurities of silver or manganese alter the colour of the emitted light, but pure stoicheiometric zinc sulphide does not phosphoresce (Fig. 6.9). This substance is used in cathode ray screens and in scintillation counters. Other solids used in scintillation counting include impure anthracene, for detecting beta particles, and sodium iodide containing a trace of thallium, for detecting gamma rays.

Electroluminescent solids, such as impure ZnS, glow when exposed to alternating electric fields whose frequency exceeds 3000 cycles sec^{-1}. They have no technical importance.

Triboluminescent solids emit light when exposed to high pressures, owing to the rapid production and elimination of defects.

Sonoluminescent solids emit light when exposed to intense sound waves.

A particularly useful luminescent solid is ruby, which is crystalline aluminium oxide containing about 2 per cent of chromium. In this

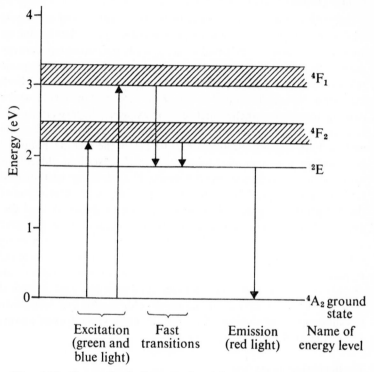

Fig. 6.10. *Energy level diagram for* Cr^{3+} *in* Al_2O_3 *[ruby]* (*after D'Haenans and Asawa, 1962*).

crystal the Cr^{3+} ion has three sharp energy levels or bands in addition to the ground state, as shown in Fig. 6.10. When exposed to green or yellow light, the ion is excited to one or other of the F levels, and can then lose its excess energy in two stages via the intermediate ^2E level, thus:

$$^4F_1 \rightarrow {}^2E + \text{vibration energy (fast)}$$
$$^4F_2 \rightarrow {}^2E + \text{vibration energy (fast)}$$
$$^2E \rightarrow {}^4A_2 + \text{red light (very fast)}$$

The light emitted is monochromatic with a wavelength of 6943 Å.

8

By using powerful flashes of light to excite nearly all the Cr^{3+} ions to the F levels, the crystal can be obtained for a short time with most of the Cr^{3+} ions in the ^2E level. In this state it acts as a monochromatic source of light of very great intensity, which is used in the commercial devices known as lasers.

Colour centres

Semiconductors are intermediate between metals and insulators with respect to the size of the forbidden energy gap. Metals have an energy gap which is very small or zero, while insulators have energy gaps of the order of 5 eV, so that they are transparent in the visible region but absorb in the ultra-violet region. It has already been mentioned that semiconduction can be induced in many insulators by making them non-stoicheiometric. For example, imperfections can be produced in an ionic solid like sodium chloride by either heating with sodium vapour, electrolysing just below the melting point, or bombarding with gamma radiation. Imperfect sodium chloride is usually coloured pink and may luminesce. The colour can be destroyed by heating the crystal below the melting point, or by electrolysis of the hot solid, when the colour moves slowly to the anode and disappears. Many types of defect are probably present in these imperfect crystals. The best understood are those associated with a missing chloride anion, whose vacant position in the lattice may be occupied by an electron. This electron is released by heating or dissolution, and gives rise to the abnormal colour, luminescence, and electrical conductivity. Other defects in sodium chloride may be associated with the substitution of Cl_2^- and Cl_3^- for Cl^- anions; the former anions can be detected by their spectra.

The photographic process

Silver bromide is a semiconductor whose response to visible light is of great importance in photography. A photosensitive film consists of a thin layer of gelatine in which are embedded small crystals of silver bromide, which contain sulphur atoms as a lattice impurity. If this film is exposed to light it shows no visible change, but if it is then treated in the dark with a reducing agent such as hydroquinone, known as the developer, the exposed portions turn black owing to the deposition of particles of silver. It can be shown that gaseous bromine is given off in the process, so that the overall reaction is

$$2AgBr \xrightarrow[\text{2. } C_6H_4(OH)_2]{\text{1. light}} 2Ag + Br_2$$

A hypothesis which accounts for the observations is the following one. Exposure to light excites electrons in the silver bromide lattice, so that these electrons become mobile until they are trapped by impurities such as sulphur atoms. The trapped electron then attracts a silver ion and reduces it to form a silver atom. The silver ions are known to be unusually mobile in silver halides (see page 69). By repetition of this process, a single sulphur or impurity atom can concentrate many silver atoms round it. The developer supplies electrons to the sulphur atoms, amplifying the original process by a factor of 10^5 to produce a speck of silver, the 'photographic grain'. The efficiency of the process can be gauged by the fact that only 5 or 10 photons of light are needed to form a detectable grain.

Colloidal metal particles are also formed by bombarding ionic solids like sodium chloride with fast electrons.

Thermal conduction

Heat is conducted mainly by the vibrations of the atoms, and scarcely at all by the excited electrons, in semiconductors. The rather complicated dependence of thermal conductivity on temperature can now be accounted for theoretically (Goldsmid, 1965).

Electrical conduction

In intrinsic semiconductors the number of conduction electrons is equal to the number of positive holes, and since electrons are more mobile than holes they carry the bulk of the current. The electrons also carry most of the current in n-type semiconductors, as they do in metals, but in p-type semiconductors the holes contribute most to the electrical conductivity. The conductivity, like the number of conduction electrons, is proportional to $e^{-E/kT}$, where E is the forbidden energy gap. In practice, the conductivity is extraordinarily sensitive to impurities, as is shown by the fact that the addition of 1 part of boron to 10^5 parts of silicon increases the conductivity of the latter by a factor of a thousand. This is one reason for the large amount of current research into methods of obtaining the chemical elements in the form of large crystals of high purity.

The rapid variation of electrical conductivity with temperature is a feature of semiconductors such as germanium (Fig. 1.16) or triferric tetroxide. These materials are used as compact, sensitive, and rapidly responding thermometers, usually known as *thermistors*.

The Hall effect

A useful experimental method of distinguishing n-type and p-type semiconductors, and of measuring the number of conduction electrons and/or positive holes, makes use of the Hall effect (Fig. 6.11). If a

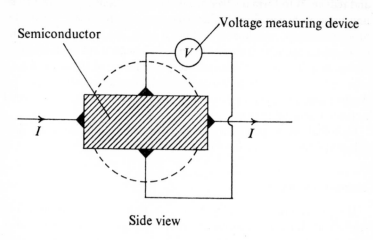

Side view

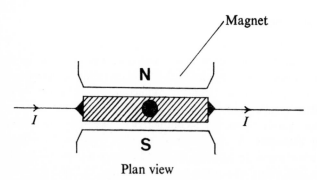

Plan view

Fig. 6.11. Diagram of the Hall effect in a semiconducting crystal.

current I is applied to a crystal in the x-direction, and a magnetic field of strength H in the z-direction, a potential difference V is generated between opposite faces of the crystal perpendicular to the y-direction. The number N of conduction electrons (or holes in a p-type semiconductor) is given by

$$N = IH/Ved \quad \text{(mks units)}$$

where e is the electronic charge and d is the thickness of the crystal in the z-direction. If N is positive, the semiconductor is p-type, while if N is negative the conductor is n-type. N is of the order of 10^{15}–10^{19} conduction electrons or holes per cm^3 for most semiconductors. It can be measured independently by electron spin resonance techniques.

In practice, difficulties arise in measuring the Hall effect because of the contact resistance at the junction of a metal and a semiconductor. In some cases, the surface conductivity may exceed the bulk conductivity and give rise to errors.

Photoconductivity

It has been shown that absorption of energy exceeding the forbidden energy gap will cause insulators to conduct electricity. For example, solid selenium has an energy gap in the visible region and becomes a conductor on exposure to visible light. It is said to be *photoconducting*, and crystals of selenium are used to detect and measure the intensity of visible light in devices called *photocells*. Other semiconductors such as lead sulphide are used to detect infra-red radiation using the same principle. The rate of decay of photoconductivity when the exciting source is removed measures the rate of recombination of electrons and positive holes, which is a first order process when there are many more electrons than holes, or vice-versa. Another type of photocell consists of a junction between p-type and n-type forms of a semiconductor, which generates a current on exposure to radiation. Thus a junction between p-type and n-type silicon is sensitive to visible light, and is used in exposure meters and solar batteries. Similar junctions made of germanium and indium antimonide are used as detectors of near and far infra-red radiation respectively.

Photoelectric emission

Like metals, semiconductors will emit electrons when exposed to radiation whose energy exceeds the work function. Many semiconductors have lower work functions than do metals, and in a few of these the efficiency of photoelectric emission exceeds that of metals by many orders of magnitude. Thus p-type Cs_3Sb has a work function of only 1·8 eV, and therefore emits electrons when exposed to radiation whose wavelength is shorter than 6800 Å, i.e., green, blue, and ultra-violet light. For this material the quantum efficiency is about 25 per cent, and the current of electrons emitted on exposure to visible light is between 20 and 50 μA per lumen.

Thermoelectric emission

When semiconductors with small work functions are heated, they emit electrons at much lower temperatures than do metals. For example, an n-type mixture of CaO, SrO, and BaO emits electrons when heated to 1000°K, and is used in the heated cathodes of certain electronic valves. Similar materials can be used in the *field emission microscope* (Fig. 6.12), in which a pointed crystal at a high negative potential is heated *in vacuo*. Electrons emitted by the point in the high

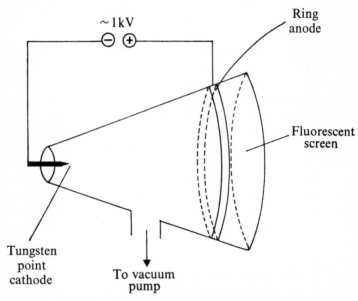

Fig. 6.12. Diagram of field emission microscope.

field gradient are accelerated by the potential to an earthed, luminescent screen. Here they form an enlarged image of the point, showing individual planes of atoms. As the crystal evaporates, imperfections and dislocations are revealed on the screen.

Secondary electron emission

The bombardment of semiconductors with primary electrons causes the emission of secondary electrons; metals behave similarly. However, for some primary electron energies, more secondary electrons are emitted than primary electrons are absorbed, so the effect can be used in devices for amplification of electron currents. Such a device is the electron multiplier, which consists of about twelve cathodes of copper beryllide which can bombard one another in a cascade. An electron of 150 eV energy can produce about four secondary electrons on striking a cathode. Thus, by maintaining a potential difference of about 150 V between each electrode it is possible to amplify a small current by a factor of 10^6.

Other semiconductors, such as ZnS, become conducting when bombarded with electrons in an applied electric field. They have been used for counting electrons and other nuclear particles.

Dielectric breakdown

All insulators conduct electricity when placed in sufficiently strong electric fields. This is known as *dielectric breakdown*, and may be due

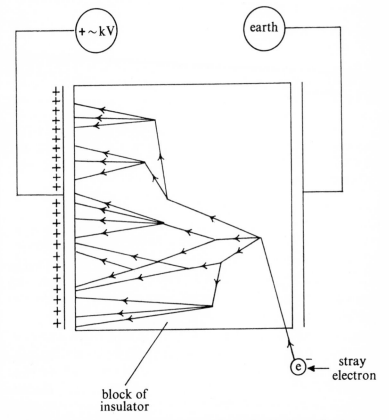

Fig. 6.13. *Diagram illustrating avalanche conduction by an insulating solid in a very large electric field gradient.*

to several different causes, not all of which are fully understood. The critical potential difference which an insulator can withstand is strongly dependent on the one- and two-dimensional imperfections in the crystal tested, and also on the presence of polarizable atoms, dipoles, and impurities which may have energy levels in the forbidden energy gap. The process of dielectric breakdown can be visualized by considering what happens to a single free electron in an insulator subjected to a large electric field. The electron is accelerated towards the anode, and may gain sufficient kinetic energy from the field to create many electron/hole pairs by excitation along its path. These secondary electrons repeat the same cycle, leading to an avalanche of electrons analogous to the ionization of gas molecules in a Geiger counter. Amplification factors of up to 10^6 secondary electrons per primary electron may be involved (Fig. 6.13).

Magnetic properties

Semiconductors are normally diamagnetic at low temperatures. As the temperature rises, electrons excited to the lowest unfilled band are mostly unpaired, giving rise to a weak paramagnetism which increases exponentially with temperature. Unpaired electrons in semiconductors can be detected by their electron spin resonance signals.

A few semiconductors containing transition metals are ferrimagnetic (e.g., $Fe_{0.9}S$) or antiferromagnetic (e.g., FeS). The technically important ferrites (e.g., Fe_3O_4), whose magnetic properties have been discussed in chapter 4, are mostly semiconductors.

The semiconductor InSb is used to measure the strengths of magnetic fields by applying the Hall effect. A calibrated crystal with four contacts is used (Fig. 6.11). This is placed with the magnetic field along the z-axis, and a known current is passed through it along the x-axis. The potential difference across the crystal which is generated along the y-axis is a measure of the magnetic field strength.

Catalysis

Some semiconductors act as catalysts, and a few are of great technical importance for this purpose. Catalysis is largely a surface effect, but it seems likely that defects in both the surface and the bulk of the crystal may be involved. The process of catalysis of an addition reaction between two molecules A and B is envisaged as follows:

$$\text{Overall reaction: } A + B \rightarrow AB$$

Step 1. Adsorption of A and B from the gas phase on to the solid surface.

Step 2. Charge transfer from the solid:

$$A \rightarrow A^+ + e^-$$
$$B \rightarrow B^- + h^+$$

where e^- is an electron in the lowest filled band, and h^+ a positive hole in the upper filled band.

Step 3. The electron and hole diffuse into, and annihilate in, the bulk of the solid.

Step 4. $\qquad A^+ + B^- \rightarrow AB$ on the surface.

Step 5. AB desorbs.

Step 4 is usually the slowest step which determines the overall rate of reaction, but step 3 may be quite slow in germanium and other semiconductors.

Experimentally, it is found that oxidation reactions involving gaseous oxygen are best catalysed by p-type semiconductors, while hydrogenations and dehydrogenations are best catalysed by n-type semiconductors. For example, p-type CuO, Cu_2O, or NiO are used to catalyse the oxidations

$$2CO + O_2 \rightleftharpoons 2CO_2$$

and

$$2N_2 + O_2 \rightleftharpoons 2N_2O$$

On the other hand, the reactions

$$H_2 + D_2 \rightleftharpoons 2HD$$

and

$$H_2 + C_2H_4 \rightleftharpoons C_2H_6$$

are catalysed by n-type semiconductors and by metals. The Al_2O_3/Cr_2O_3 catalysts used industrially to dehydrogenate cyclohexane and butane have been found to change from p-type to n-type during the process. Catalysts for hydrations and dehydrations, such as

$$C_2H_4 + H_2O \rightleftharpoons C_2H_5OH$$

include MgO, Al_2O_3, and SiO_2, but it is still not clear whether their catalytic power is related to their semiconducting properties.

Appendix
Symmetry and crystal notation

A set of elements $e_1, e_2, \ldots e_i, \ldots e_n$ are said to form an *Abelian Group* if four conditions apply:

1. There is a relation between any pair of elements such that

$$e_i.e_j = e_k$$

for all values of i and j; that is, the relation maps the set of all pairs of elements onto the set of elements itself.

2. There exists an identity element e_1 such that

$$e_1.e_i = e_i$$

for every value of i.

3. The associative law applies, i.e.

$$(e_i.e_j).e_k = e_i.(e_j.e_k)$$

4. The commutative law applies, i.e.

$$e_i.e_j = e_j.e_i$$

for every value of i and j.

The properties of Abelian Groups form a branch of mathematics, and here we will only state two important theorems without proving them.

Theorem 1. The set of operations mapping a three-dimensional object onto itself forms an Abelian Group.

Theorem 2. In three-dimensional space the number of Abelian Groups mapping different objects onto themselves is finite and calculable.

The operations which map an object onto itself are:

1. Reflection in a mirror plane (symbol m).

2. Rotation about an n-fold axis (symbol n).

3. Inversion about a point called the centre of symmetry (symbol $\bar{1}$). If the point is taken to be the origin, inversion is the operation which maps any point with co-ordinates (x, y, z) onto $(-x, -y, -z)$.

4. Rotation-inversion, or rotation about an n-fold axis followed by inversion about a point (symbol $\bar{n}$).

As far as unit cells of crystals are concerned, the only possible axes of symmetry are 2-, 3-, 4-, and 6-fold axes. With this restriction, theorem 2 can be made more explicit, and it can be shown that there are only thirty-two different ways of combining symmetry operations for unit cells, or thirty-two *point groups*. These are usually described by the Hermann-Mauguin notation, as follows. First write down the order of the principal axis of rotation or rotation-inversion, n or $\bar{n}$. If there is a two-fold axis of symmetry perpendicular to the principal axis, add 2 thus, $n2$ or $\bar{n}2$. If there is a mirror plane which contains the principal axis, add m. If there is a mirror plane perpendicular to the principal axis, add $/m$. If there are mirror planes containing the principal axis and perpendicular to it, add $/mm$.

The thirty-two point groups have been classified into seven *crystallographic systems*, as shown in Table A.1. For a whole crystal there exist additional symmetry elements to those found for the unit cell. These map the crystal onto itself by a translation coupled with either rotation or reflection. The elements are known as screw axes and glide planes. A *screw axis* n_p involves rotation by $2\pi/n$ radians coupled with translation by $1/p$th of that side of the unit cell which is parallel to the axis of rotation. p can take the values $1, 2, \ldots$ $(n-1)$. A *glide plane* involves translation coupled with reflection. When allowance is made for all possible screw axes and glide planes, it is found that there are two hundred and thirty distinct ways of combining symmetry operations for whole crystals, and these are known as *space groups*. Finding the crystallographic system, point

Table A.1

The crystallographic systems

Crystallographic system	Unit cell sides	Unit cell angles	Minimum symmetry	No. of point groups	No. of space groups	Examples
Cubic	$a=b=c$	$\alpha=\beta=\gamma=90°$	4×3-fold axes	5	26	Au, diamond, NaCl, alum
Orthorhombic	$a \neq b \neq c$	$\alpha=\beta=\gamma=90°$	3×2-fold axes or one 2-fold axis $+2$ mirror planes	3	59	α-S, KNO_3
Hexagonal	$a=b \neq c$	$\alpha=\beta=90°$ $\gamma=120°$	one 6- or $\bar{6}$-fold axis	7	22	Zn, graphite, ice
Tetragonal	$a=b \neq c$	$\alpha=\beta=\gamma=90°$	one 4- or $\bar{4}$-fold axis	7	68	Sn, TiO_2
Rhombohedral	$a=b=c$	$\alpha=\beta=\gamma \neq 90°$	one 3-fold axis	5	30	SiO_2, $CaCO_3$
Monoclinic	$a \neq b \neq c$	$\alpha=\gamma=90°$ $\beta \neq 90°$	one 2-fold axis or one mirror plane	3	13	β-S, $CaSO_4 . 2H_2O$
Triclinic	$a \neq b \neq c$	$\alpha \neq \beta \neq \gamma \neq 90°$	none	2	2	$CuSO_4 . 5H_2O$, $K_2Cr_2O_7$

group, and space group of a given crystal requires a combination of optical and X-ray examination.

Miller indices

Instead of mentally subdividing a crystal into unit cells, we can think of a crystal as a lattice of sets of parallel planes of atoms. *Miller indices* are a notation defining sets of parallel planes: they are the reciprocals of the relative intercepts on the axes expressed as integers.

In order to find the Miller indices of any set of planes, we proceed as follows. Select an origin and three axes of reference, not necessarily mutually perpendicular, but determined by the symmetry of the crystal. Next select a *unit face* as a reference face of the crystal: suppose this intersects the axes at $x=a$, $y=b$, $z=c$. Any other face of the crystal or important lattice plane can be specified by the Miller indices (h, k, l) if the plane intersects the axes at $x=a/h$, $y=b/k$, $z=c/l$. It can be shown that (h, k, l) is equivalent to (nh, nk, nl) for any value of n, and it is conventional to choose n so that h, k, and l are all integers. If the plane chosen does not intersect the x-axis, $h=0$ and so on.

The *law of rational indices* states that h, k, and l are *small* integers for crystal faces and other important lattice planes. This is a natural consequence of the high density of lattice points in the faces of a crystal.

Further reading

This list includes most of the books and reviews that I have found useful in preparing the present book, but is by no means exhaustive. Books marked with an * are either brief or non-mathematical, and are particularly recommended for students with relatively little background in this field.

Chapter 1: *General*

*Azaroff, L. V. *An introduction to solids*. McGraw-Hill, 1960.
Dekker, A. J. *Solid state physics*. Prentice Hall, 1957.
*Galwey, A. K. *Chemistry of solids*. Science Paperbacks, 1967.
Kittel, C. *Introduction to solid state physics*, 2nd edition. Wiley, 1956.
*Kittel, C. *Elementary solid state physics*. Wiley, 1962.
Mandelcorn, L. *Non-stoicheiometric compounds*. Academic Press, 1964.
Mykura, H. *Solid surfaces and interfaces*. Kegan Paul, 1966.
Peierls, R. E. *Quantum theory of solids*. Oxford, 1955.
Seitz, F. *The modern theory of solids*. McGraw-Hill, 1940.
Slater, J. C. *Quantum theory of molecules and solids*, vol. 2. McGraw-Hill, 1965.
Wells, A. F. *Structural inorganic chemistry*, 3rd edition. Oxford, 1962.
*Wert, C. A. and Thomson, R. M. *Physics of solids*. McGraw-Hill, 1964.
Wyckoff, R. W. *Crystal structures*, vols. 1–5. Interscience, 1960.

Properties of solids

Barrer, R. M. *Diffusion in and through solids*. Cambridge, 1951.
Bleaney, B. I. and Bleaney, B. *Electricity and magnetism*. Oxford, 1957.

*Bowen, E. J. *Chemical aspects of light*, 2nd edition. Oxford, 1946.

Carslaw, H. S. and Jaeger, J. C. *Conduction of heat in solids*. Oxford, 1959.

Cochran, W. Lattice vibrations. *Rep. Progr. Phys.* **26**, 1, 1963.

Cusack, N. *The electrical and magnetic properties of solids*. Longmans, 1958.

*Goldsmid, H. J. *The thermal properties of solids*. Kegan Paul, 1965.

Gregg, S. J. *The surface chemistry of solids*, 2nd edition. Chapman and Hall, 1961.

Meakins, R. J. Mechanisms of dielectric absorption in solids. *Progr. in Dielectrics*, **3**, 151, 1961.

Effects of temperature and pressure

Bundy, F. P. Direct conversion of graphite to diamond in static pressure apparatus. *J. Chem. Phys.* **38**, 631, 1963.

Drickamer, H. G. The effects of high pressure on the electronic structure of solids. *Solid State Phys.* **17**, 1, 1965.

Paul, W. and Warschauer, D. M. *Solids under pressure*. McGraw-Hill, 1963.

*Scurlock, R. G. *Low temperature behaviour of solids*. Kegan Paul, 1966.

Staveley, L. A. K. Transitions in solids and liquids. *Quart. Rev.* **3**, 65, 1949.

Ubbelohde, A. R. Thermal transformations in solids. *Quart. Rev.* **11**, 246, 1957.

Ubbelohde, A. R. *Melting and crystal structure*, Oxford, 1965.

Chapter 2

Barrer, R. M. *Inorganic inclusion compounds.* (In: Mandelcorn, L., see above.)

Brophy, J. J. and Buttery, J. W. *Organic semiconductors*. Macmillan, 1962.

Brown, D. S., Wallwork, S. C., and Wilson, A. The crystal structure of the anthracene-s-trinitrobenzene complex. *Acta Cryst.* **17**, 168, 1964.

Cruikshank, D. W. J. A detailed refinement of the crystal and molecular structure of anthracene. *Acta Cryst.* **9**, 915, 1956.

Fetterly, L. C. *Organic adducts.* (In: Mandelcorn, L., see above.)

Kearns, D. R. Electronic conduction in organic molecular solids. *Adv. Chem. Phys.* **7**, 282, 1964.

Phillips, C. G. S., and Williams, R. J. P. *Inorganic chemistry.* Oxford, 1965.

Pimentel, G. C. and McClellan, A. L. *The hydrogen bond.* W. H. Freeman, 1960.

Pohl, H. A. Physico-chemical aspects of organic semiconductors. *Progr. Solid State Chem.* **1**, 316, 1964.

Powell, H. M. *Clathrates.* (In: Mandelcorn, L., see above).

Chapter 3

Berman, R. *Physical properties of diamond.* Oxford, 1965.

Goryunova, N. A. *The chemistry of diamond-like semiconductors.* Chapman and Hall, 1965.

Ubbelohde, A. R. and Lewis, F. A. *Graphite and its crystal compounds.* Oxford, 1960.

Chapter 4

Cady, W. P. *Piezoelectricity.* McGraw-Hill, 1964.

Garner, W. E. *Chemistry of the solid state.* Butterworths, 1955.

Känzig, W. Ferroelectrics and antiferroelectrics. *Solid State Phys.* **4**, 1, 1957.

Ladd, M. F. C. and Lee, W. H. Lattice energies and related topics. *Progr. Solid State Chem.* **1**, 37, 1964 and **2**, 378, 1965.

Megaw, H. D. *Ferroelectricity in crystals.* Methuen, 1957.

Mott, N. F. and Gurney, R. W. *Electronic processes in ionic crystals*, 2nd edition. Oxford, 1957.

Sonchay, M. P. *Polyanions and polycations.* Gauthier-Villars, 1963.

Stephenson, C. G. and Hooley, J. G. The heat capacity of KH_2PO_4 from 15 to 300°K. *J. Am. Chem. Soc.* **66**, 1397, 1944.

Wolf, W. P. Ferrimagnetism. *Rep. Progr. Phys.* **24**, 212, 1961.

Chapter 5

Barrett, C. S. *Structure of metals*, 2nd edition. McGraw-Hill, 1952.

Bond, G. C. *Catalysis by metals.* Academic Press, 1962.

Callaway, J. *Energy band theory.* Academic Press, 1964.

Cottrell, A. H. *Theoretical structural metallurgy.* Arnold, 1948.

*Crock, R. H. and Ebner, M. L. *Ceramics, Plastics and Metals.* D. C. Heath, 1965.

Hayward, D. O. and Trapnell, B. M. W. *Chemisorption.* Butterworths, 1964.

Hume Rothery, W. and Gaynor, G. V. *The structure of metals and alloys.* Institute of Metals, 1956.

*Lee, E. W. *Magnetism*. Pelican, 1963.

Matthias, B. T., Geballe, T. H., and Compton, V. B. Superconductivity. *Rev. Mod. Phys.* **35**, 1, 1963.

Mott, N. F. and Jones, H. *The theory of the properties of metals and alloys*. Oxford, 1936.

Smithells, C. J. *Metals reference book*, 2nd edition. Butterworths, 1955.

Trapnell, B. M. W. Specificity in catalysis by metals. *Quart. Rev.* **8**, 404, 1954.

Chapter 6

Azaroff, L. V. and Brophy, J. J. *Electronic properties in materials*. McGraw-Hill, 1963.

Ballentyne, D. W. G. The relationship of photoluminescence and electroluminescence to structure. *Progr. Solid State Chem.* **1**, 209, 1964.

D'Haenans, I. J. and Asawa, C. K. Energy levels in ruby. *J. Appl. Phys.* **33**, 3201, 1962.

Gatos, H. C. *Properties of elemental and compound semiconductors*. Interscience, 1960.

Hannay, N. B. *Semiconductors*. Reinhold, 1959.

Hulliger, F. and Mooser, E. The bond description of semiconductors. *Progr. Solid State Chem.* **2**, 330, 1964.

*Jonscher, A. K. *Solid semiconductors*. Kegan Paul, 1965.

Leverenz, H. W. *An introduction to luminescence in solids*. Wiley, 1950.

Mason, J. H. Dielectric breakdown in solid insulators. *Progr. in Dielectrics* **1**, 1, 1959.

Moss, T. S. Photoconductivity. *Rep. Progr. Phys.* **28**, 15, 1965.

Read, W. T. *Dislocations in crystals*. McGraw-Hill, 1953.

Schulman, J. H. and Compton, W. D. *Colour centres in solids*. Pergamon, 1963.

*Wright, D. A. *Semiconductors*, 3rd edition. Methuen, 1958.

Experimental methods for studying solids and their structures

Bacon, G. E. *Neutron diffraction*, 2nd edition. Oxford, 1962.

Bacon, G. E. Neutron diffraction. *Adv. Inorg. Chem. Radiochem.* **8**, 225, 1966.

Gilman, J. J. *The art and science of growing crystals*. Wiley, 1963.

Henry, N. F. M., Lipson, H. and Wooster, W. A. *The interpretation of X-ray diffraction photographs*. Macmillan, 1960.

Kerr, P. F. *Optical mineralogy*, 3rd edition. McGraw-Hill, 1959.

Lark-Horowitz, K. and Johnson, V. A. *Methods of experimental physics*, vol. 6 A & B. Academic Press, 1959.

*Lonsdale, K. *Crystals and X-rays*. Bell, 1948.

Loudon, R. The Raman effect in crystals. *Adv. Phys.* **13,** 423, 1964.

Shull, C. G. and Wollan, E. O. Applications of neutron diffraction to solid state problems. *Solid State Phys.* **2,** 137, 1956.

Weissberger, A. *Physical methods in organic chemistry*, 3rd edition. Interscience, 1960.

*Wheatley, P. J. *The determination of molecular structure*. Oxford, 1960.

Williams, D. *Methods of experimental physics*, vol. 3. Academic Press, 1962.

Glossary

absolute zero, 0°K: the lowest possible temperature, which can never be attained experimentally.

absorption spectrum: the intensity of the incident radiation absorbed as a function of the energy of the radiation.

acceptor of electrons: a substance with an affinity for electrons, such as any non-metal.

acid: a source of protons.

actinide: one of the elements Ac, Th, Pa, U, and the trans-uranic elements up to and including nobelium, all of which have a partly filled 5f-shell.

activation energy: the minimum kinetic energy needed by a molecule before it will react in a particular way.

addition reaction: a chemical reaction in which two or more molecules react to give a single molecule as a product.

adsorption: the binding of molecules on a solid surface.

alkali metal: one of the elements Li, Na, K, Rb, or Cs.

alkaline earth: one of the elements Ca, Sr, Ba, or Ra.

allotropy: another term for polymorphism.

alloy: a substance with metallic conductivity containing two or more elements, at least one of which is a metal.

alpha particles: helium-4 nuclei emitted during radioactive decay.

A metals: the elements K, Ca, Sc, Ti, V, Cr, Mn, and their homologues in the fourth and fifth periods (Rb–Tc) and Cs–Re).

amorphous: lacking symmetry.

ampere, A: a unit of electric current equal to 1 coulomb sec^{-1}.

amplification: occurs when the response to a stimulus exceeds the stimulus in magnitude.

123

Ångstrom unit, Å: 10^{-8} cm.

anion: a negatively charged ion.

anisotropic: with properties whose magnitude depends on the axis of measurement.

anneal: to even out by heating.

anode: a positively charged electrode, at which oxidation occurs.

antiferroelectric: of a crystal containing arrays of spontaneously polarized ions with neighbouring arrays polarized in the opposite sense (see page 71).

antiferromagnetic: of a crystal containing arrays of atoms with unpaired electrons, with their magnetic moments oriented so as to oppose one another (see page 73).

antiprism: a geometrical figure with either six or eight apices (see Fig. 4.6).

aromatic ring: a planar ring of carbon atoms containing single and double bonds, with an abnormally high heat of combustion.

atmosphere: a unit of pressure equal to $1 \cdot 013 \times 10^6$ dynes cm^{-2}.

atom: the smallest particle of an element that retains the properties of that element.

Avogadro's number: the number of molecules in the molecular weight in grams of any substance, i.e., $6 \cdot 02252 \times 10^{23}$.

axis: a straight line in a fixed direction.

band: a continuous range of energies, either of a solid or its spectrum.

bar: a unit of pressure equal to 10^6 dynes cm^{-2} or $0 \cdot 987$ atmosphere.

beta particles: electrons emitted during radioactive decay.

binding energy: the energy needed to vaporize a solid to its constituent atoms or molecules.

B metals: the elements Cu, Zn, Ga, Ge, As, and their homologues in the fourth and fifth periods (Ag–Sb) and (Au–Bi).

Body-centred cubic: a common type of unit cell (shown in Fig. 5.1).

Boltzmann's constant, k: $1 \cdot 38054 \times 10^{-16}$ erg deg^{-1}.

Boltzmann statistics: the statistics of distinguishable particles: the number of ways in which N particles can be divided into p subsets such that the ith subset contains n particles is $N \prod\limits_{i=1}^{p} n_i!$.

Born-Haber cycle: a method of finding lattice energies of ionic solids (see page 64).

calorie: a unit of energy equal to $4 \cdot 1867 \times 10^7$ ergs.

catalyst: a substance which increases the rate of a reaction, and which can be recovered at the end of the reaction and used again.

cathode: a negatively charged electrode, at which reduction occurs.

cathode rays: electrons emitted from a cathode *in vacuo*.

cathodoluminescence: luminescence excited by electron impact.

cation: a positively charged ion.

centre of symmetry: a point in a unit cell, inversion about which maps the cell onto itself.

charge transfer: the transfer of an electron from one atom or ion to another.

chemical bond: an ionic, covalent, or intermediate type of bond with an energy exceeding 10 kcals mole^{-1}.

Clapeyron relation: a thermodynamic identity which holds for first order transitions (see page 11).

cleavage: the manner in which a crystal splits in response to a stress.

colour: the possession of an absorption spectrum in the visible region.

complex ion: an ion containing more than one atom.

compressibility: the rate of change of volume with pressure per unit volume, i.e., $-V^{-1}(\partial V/\partial p)_T$.

conductivity (electrical): the reciprocal of the resistivity.

co-ordination number: the number of nearest neighbours to an atom or ion.

coulomb: a unit of electrical charge equal to $6 \cdot 25 \times 10^{18}$ electronic charges.

covalent bond: a bond between two atoms in which two valency electrons are shared by each atom.

covalent solid: a solid in which the covalent bonds extend indefinitely in 1, 2, or 3 dimensions.

crystal: a solid possessing symmetry.

cubic close-packed: a common type of unit cell (shown in Fig. 2.1).

Curie temperature: the temperature above which ferromagnetism is lost.

current: the rate of movement of electrical charge in a fixed direction.

cyclohexanoid: containing C_6 rings which are non-planar, as in cyclohexane.

defect: an error and/or an impurity in an ordered lattice of atoms.

degree Kelvin (°K): $1°K = 1/273 \cdot 16$ part of the temperature of melting ice at a pressure of 1 atmosphere.

dehydration: removal of water or the elements of water.

dehydrogenation: removal of hydrogen.

d-electrons: electrons with a secondary quantum number $l = 2$, whose charge density pattern has two nodes.

density: mass per unit volume.

desorption: loss of molecules from a solid surface.

developer: a reducing agent used in photography.

diamagnetic: repelled by magnetic fields.

dielectric breakdown: the conduction of electricity by an insulator in an electric field of great intensity (see page 111).

dielectric constant: the ratio of the force between two fixed electrical charges *in vacuo* to the force between the same charges separated by the substance of interest.

diffraction: the scattering of waves by obstacles whose size is comparable to the wavelength.

dimer: the product of the addition of two identical molecules or monomers.

dipole: a molecule or bond with an unequal distribution of charge along one axis; or, two electrical charges of equal magnitude but opposite sign, separated by a small distance.

dipole moment: the product of one of the charges of a dipole and the distance between the charges.

dispersion: the splitting of polychromatic light into a spectrum.

dissociation energy: the energy needed in splitting a molecule into its constituent atoms.

dissolution: the process of dissolving one substance in another to form a homogeneous phase.

divalent: with a valency of 2.

dodecahedron: a regular figure with twenty apices and twelve pentagonal faces (Fig. 2.13).

domain: a more or less perfectly ordered region in a crystal.

donor of electrons: a substance which readily gives up its electrons, e.g., a metal.

double refraction: occurs when the velocity of light in a crystal varies with the direction of vibration of the light.

ductile: able to be pulled into wires.

dyne: a unit of force, which would accelerate 1 g by 1 cm sec^{-2}.

edge dislocation: a one-dimensional crystal defect (see Fig. 6.2).

elasticity: the property whereby a solid recovers from a stress which deforms it.

electric field: the strength F (or intensity) of an electric field is measured by the force in dynes which it exerts on a unit positive charge: the energy of an electric field is $DF^2/8\pi$, where D is the dielectric constant.

electrode: a piece of metal, or graphite, bearing an electric charge.

electrode potential: the potential difference between a metal electrode in a solution containing unit activity of metal ions, and a hydrogen electrode at one atmosphere pressure in a solution containing unit activity of protons.

electroluminescence: luminescence caused by an alternating electric field.

electron: a fundamental particle with mass $9 \cdot 1 \times 10^{-28}$ g, an electric charge of $-1 \cdot 6 \times 10^{-19}$ coulombs and a magnetic moment of $-9 \cdot 3 \times 10^{-21}$ erg oersted^{-1}.

electron affinity: the energy evolved on adding an electron to an atom or molecule.

electron deficient: with fewer electrons than required by classical valency theory.

electron mobility: the mean velocity of an electron divided by the strength of the applied electric field.

electron overlap: the binding that occurs when electron shells from adjacent atoms overlap spatially.

electron shell: a set of electrons in an atom with the same values of the principal and secondary quantum numbers n and l.

electron spin: a two-valued property of an electron related to its magnetic moment.

electron spin resonance: a technique for measuring the number of unpaired electrons in a sample, based on the intensity of the transition from one electron spin state to the other.

electron volt, eV: a unit of energy equal to $1 \cdot 602 \times 10^{-12}$ ergs; 1 eV atom$^{-1} = 23 \cdot 061$ kcals mole^{-1}.

electronegativity: a measure of non-metallic character.

electronics: the science of the behaviour of electrons in materials, which has many industrial applications.

electronic spectrum: the energy transitions involving the excitation of electrons in molecules above the ground state: it usually occurs in the ultra-violet or visible region.

electropositivity: a measure of metallic character, i.e., electron donating power.

electrostatic force: the force between two electrically charged objects.

element: a substance which cannot be broken down chemically into simpler components.

energy level: one of the discrete energy states an atom can possess in accordance with quantum theory.

entropy, S: a measure of the order in a system. $S = k\log_e P$, where k is Boltzmann's constant and P is the probability of the particular state of the system.

erg: a unit of energy equal to 1 dyne cm.

excitation: the change from a lower energy state to a higher one by absorption of energy.

extrinsic semiconductor: a solid which becomes a semiconductor only when impure and/or non-stoicheiometric.

far infra-red: electromagnetic radiation with energy between 0·001 and 0·1 eV.

f-electrons: electrons with a secondary quantum number $l=3$, whose charge density pattern has three nodes.

Fermi-Dirac statistics: the statistics of indistinguishable particles obeying the Pauli principle.

ferrimagnetism: a property of insulators containing unpaired d- or f-electrons in two distinct types of site, whose magnetic moments are oriented so that they do not cancel out.

ferrite: a compound of formula LM_2O_4, where L and M are trivalent and divalent transition metals respectively.

ferromagnetism: a property of metals containing unpaired d- or f-electrons, whose magnetic moments are oriented spontaneously to give each perfect crystal a large magnetic susceptibility.

field emission microscope: a device for magnifying the image of a point by a factor of about 10^6 (see page 110).

first order process: a reaction whose rate is proportional to the number of particles left unreacted.

first order transition: a transition during which the density, entropy, and heat content change discontinuously when plotted against temperature (see page 10).

fluorescence: the emission of light in less than 10^{-3} sec after excitation.

fluorine bonding: a weak form of electrostatic bonding found in a few molecular fluorides (see page 33).

fluoro-anion: a complex anion containing fluorine ligands.

forbidden energy gap: the energy range between the upper filled band and the lowest unfilled band in a solid.

free radical: an atom, molecule, or ion containing unpaired electrons; most free radicals contain an odd number of electrons, at least one of which must be unpaired.

Frenkel defect: a point defect in crystals involving both a hole and an interstitial atom in a lattice (see Fig. 6.1).

frequency: the reciprocal of the time interval of a periodic disturbance or wave.

friction: the resistance to sliding motion between two adjacent surfaces.

gamma radiation: electromagnetic radiation with energy between $0 \cdot 1$ and 10 MeV, produced by nuclear reactions or radioactive decay.

gas: a state of matter in which the constituent particles are free to move and have negligible interaction energies.

Geiger counter: a device for counting ionizing particles.

gradual transition: a transition in which the entropy, density, and heat content change gradually, and the specific heat rises to a maximum value (see page 11).

ground state: the lowest energy level of an atom or molecule.

group: usually refers to the Group in the Periodic Table of Elements.

half-life: the time taken for half the atoms or molecules undergoing a reaction to react.

Hall effect: if a current is passed through a conductor along the x-axis with a magnetic field along the z-axis, a potential difference is generated between opposite faces of the conductor along the y-axis (see Fig. 6.11).

halogen: one of the elements F, Cl, Br, or I.

harmonic motion: periodic motion in which the restoring force is proportional to the distance of the displacement from equilibrium.

heat content (enthalpy): a property equal to the internal energy $+pV$, where p is the pressure and V the volume.

heat of formation: the heat evolved when 1 mole of substance is produced from its elements in their normal states at NTP.

heat of solvation: the heat evolved when 1 mole of a substance, or ion, is dissolved in a large excess of solvent.

heterogeneous: in more than one phase.

heteropolyacid: complex ionic salts formed by some oxo-anions with molybdates, niobates, tantalates, or tungstates (see page 61).

hexagonal close-packed: a common arrangement of atoms (for unit cell see Fig. 2.2).

hydration: the process of adding water or the elements of water.

hydrogenation: the addition of H_2.

hydrogen bond: a weak interaction between two electronegative atoms with a proton between them (see page 30).

hydrostatic pressure: pressure produced by compressing a column of liquid.

hysteresis: the irreversible absorption of energy during a transition.

inclusion compound: a solid compound in which molecules of one kind are trapped in holes in the crystal lattice of another kind of molecule.

inert gas: one of the elements He, Ne, Ar, Kr, Xe, or Rn.

inert pair: a pair of valency electrons, which are attached to an atom and may or may not be used in forming chemical bonds.

infra-red: electromagnetic radiation with an energy between 0·001 and 1·7 eV.

insulator: a substance whose electrical resistivity exceeds 10^{12} ohm cm.

intensive property: a property independent of volume of sample.

interstitial compound: a solid containing small atoms of one kind in the interstices of close-packed atoms of another kind (see page 80).

intrinsic semiconductor: a solid which is a semiconductor when pure and stoicheiometric.

inversion: the operation of mapping every point (x, y, z) on to the point $(-x, -y, -z)$.

ion: an atom or molecule with an electrical charge.

ion-exchanger: a solid which can exchange some of its ions with a solution without dissolving.

ionic radius: an estimate of the size of an ion.

ionic solid: a solid containing discrete ions, held together by electrostatic energy.

ionization: the loss of electrons by an atom or molecule to form an ion.

ionization energy (or potential): the energy needed to remove an electron from an atom or molecule *in vacuo*.

isomorphous: two solids are isomorphous if they contain a similar arrangement of geometrically similar particles in their unit cells.

isotropic: having no properties which depend on the axis of measurement.

kilo- (prefix): $\times 10^3$.

kinetic theory of gases: the hypothesis that gases consist of a large number of small, perfectly elastic, moving molecules.

lambda-type transition: a gradual transition during which the specific heat rises to a sharp maximum.

lanthanides: the elements La–Lu, with atomic numbers 57–71.

laser: a device in which a substance is exposed to incident radiation and emits an amplified fluorescent radiation (see page 105).

latent heat: the heat absorbed during a transition without change of temperature.

lattice: a three-dimensional array.

lattice energy: the energy needed to convert an ionic solid into gaseous ions.

ligand: one of the X groups in a molecule or complex ion of formula AX_n.

liquid: a state of matter in which the constituent particles are free to move, but interact with sufficient energy to keep any sample a constant volume, but not a constant shape.

London forces: the force between neutral atoms caused by electrostatic interactions between temporarily non-zero dipoles (see page 27).

lone pair: a pair of valency electrons attached to an atom, which may or may not be used for bonding, but whose position is oriented along a fixed axis.

lumen: a unit of light intensity.

luminescence: the emission of light following excitation.

macroscopic: of a substance in bulk, containing a large number of atoms.

Madelung constant: a geometrical factor, with a fixed numerical value for each type of unit cell, used in calculating lattice energies.

magnetic field: the strength H of a magnetic field is measured by the force in dynes which it exerts on a unit magnetic pole; the energy of a magnetic field is equal to $PH^2/8\pi$, where P is the magnetic permeability of the medium.

magnetic moment: if a magnet consists of two poles of pole strength m and $-m$, separated by a distance r, the magnetic moment is mr.

magnetic permeability: the ratio of the force between two fixed magnetic poles *in vacuo* and the force between the same poles separated by the substance of interest.

magnetic pole: two unit magnetic poles 1 cm apart *in vacuo* repel one another with a force of one dyne.

magnetic pole strength: the force in dynes between any pole and a unit pole 1 cm distant *in vacuo*.

malleable: bendable without breaking.

mega- (prefix): $\times 10^6$.

melting: the transition between solid and liquid phases of a pure substance.

metal: 1. (solid); a solid with metallic lustre, and a high electrical conductivity which decreases with rise in temperature (see chapter 5).

2. (atom); an atom with few valency electrons in its outer shell, which it readily loses to oxidizing agents.

micro- (prefix): $\times 10^{-6}$.

micron: a unit of length, $= 10^{-4}$ cm.

microwaves: electromagnetic radiation with energy between 4×10^{-5} and 10^{-3} eV.

mixed crystals: solids containing lattices consisting of two or more kinds of atom or ion arranged at random.

mole: the molecular weight in grams.

molecular sieve: a solid containing channels permeable to some molecules but not to others.

molecular solid: a solid consisting of discrete atoms or molecules, separated by regions of negligible electron density (see chapter 2).

molecular weight: the sum of the atomic weights of all the atoms in a molecule.

molecule: the smallest particle of a substance which retains the properties of that substance.

monatomic: containing one atom only.

monochromatic: consisting of one energy, or a narrow range of energies.

Néel temperature: the temperature at which antiferromagnetism is lost.

nematic: containing long molecules ordered in thread-like arrays.

neutron: a fundamental particle with a mass of $1 \cdot 675 \times 10^{-24}$ g, zero electric charge, and a magnetic moment of $-9 \cdot 6 \times 10^{-24}$ erg oersted^{-1}.

noble: of a metal which will not react with acids.

NTP: normal temperature and pressure, that is, about 273°K and 1 atmosphere.

n-type semiconductor: a semiconductor with a slight excess of valency electrons, which conduct electricity.

nuclear magnetism: the magnetic moment of any nucleus with an odd number of (protons + neutrons) is not zero, but has only about 10^{-3} of the magnitude of electronic magnetic moments.

octahedron: a regular figure with six apices and eight faces (see Fig. 4.8).

oersted: a unit of magnetic field strength, equal to the field strength 1 cm from a unit pole *in vacuo*.

ohm: a unit of electrical resistance, equal to 1 volt ampere^{-1}.

optical activity: ability to rotate the plane of polarization of light.

orbital: the volume of space occupied by an electron in an atom or molecule.

order-disorder transition: the change from a regular arrangement of atoms in a solid to a random one (see Fig. 1.14).

oxidizing agent: a substance with an affinity for electrons.

oxo-anion: a complex anion containing oxygen atoms as ligands.

paramagnetic: attracted by a magnetic field.

parameter: a physical variable.

Pauli principle: no two electrons in an atom may have the same values of the four quantum numbers n, l, m, and s.

p-electrons: electrons with a secondary quantum number $l=1$, whose charge density pattern has a single node.

pentagonal bipyramid: a geometrical figure with seven apices (see Fig. 4.6).

period: usually refers to the Periodic Table of Elements.

peroxy-salt: a salt whose anion contains O_2 ligands.

phase: a homogeneous state of matter.

phosphorescence: luminescence in which emission follows excitation after a delay exceeding 10^{-3} sec, but the delay may be greater than this.

photocell: a device used to measure light intensity.

photoconduction: conduction of electricity on exposure to radiation.

photoelectric effect or emission: emission of electrons when exposed to radiation.

photoluminescence: emission of light when exposed to radiation.

photon: a quantum of radiation energy, with zero rest mass and zero electric charge.

pi-bond: a form of bonding between atoms or molecules involving the overlapping of pi-electron orbitals.

pi-electrons: electrons in molecules whose orbitals have a single node, and which may be shared by more than two atoms.

pi-orbitals: the volume of space occupied by pi-electrons in molecules; they have at least two planes of symmetry intersecting in an axial node.

10

piezoelectricity: the development of electric charge on opposite faces of a compressed crystal, which occurs for crystals without a centre of symmetry (page 51).

planar: with the atoms in one plane.

Planck's constant: h, the energy of radiation divided by its frequency, $= 6 \cdot 625 \times 10^{-27}$ erg sec.

point defect: the loss or displacement of a single atom in a crystal lattice (Fig. 6.1).

polarizability: the dipole moment induced by a unit electric field.

polychromatic: consisting of more than one energy.

polycyclic: consisting of more than one ring.

polymer: the product of the addition of many similar molecules together.

polymorphism: the ability to exist in more than one form.

positive hole: when an electron is excited out of the upper filled band of a semiconductor, it leaves behind a positive hole in this band.

potential difference: the energy needed to transfer unit positive charge between two points measures the potential difference between them.

potential energy: energy available for doing work.

precessional energy: if an electron moves in an elliptical path round a nucleus, the axis of this ellipse does not remain fixed but rotates with a certain frequency called the precessional frequency, $= h^{-1} \times$ precessional energy.

pressure: a measure of the energy of molecules at the surface of a gas, equal to force per unit area.

promoter: an impurity which improves the functioning of a solid catalyst.

proton: a fundamental particle with a mass of $1 \cdot 673 \times 10^{-24}$ g, an electric charge of $+ 1 \cdot 6 \times 10^{-9}$ coulombs, and a magnetic moment of $1 \cdot 41 \times 10^{-23}$ erg oersted^{-1}.

p-type semiconductor: an electron-deficient semiconductor with a slight excess of positive holes, which conduct electricity.

pyroelectricity: the development of electrical charge on opposite faces of a heated crystal (see page 51).

pyro-salt: a salt formed by condensation between two hydroxo- or oxo-anions with elimination of water.

quantum efficiency: the number of molecules chemically changed divided by the number of photons absorbed.

quantum number: an integer which determines the number of units, or quanta, of angular momentum which an electron may possess in an electric or magnetic field.

quantum theory: the hypothesis that energy, and also momentum, occurs in discrete amounts or quanta in both matter and radiation.

radioactivity: the spontaneous decay of certain nuclei.

radio waves: electromagnetic radiation with an energy less than $0·00004$ eV.

radius ratio: the radius of the smaller ion divided by the radius of the larger ion for a binary ionic solid.

Raman spectrum: the spectrum obtained when a substance scatters monochromatic radiation.

reducing agent: a substance which accepts electrons.

reflectivity: the ability to reflect radiation.

refractive index: the ratio of the velocity of light *in vacuo* to the velocity of light in the substance of interest.

refractory: resistant to heat.

resistance, electrical: the potential difference across a conductor divided by the current through it.

resistivity: the electrical resistance of a uniform conductor multiplied by its cross-sectional area and divided by its length.

resonance frequency: (see page 51).

rotation-inversion: rotation about an axis followed by inversion in a centre of symmetry.

rotation spectra: spectra arising from the rotational energy levels of molecules, which occur in the far infra-red and microwave regions.

Schottky defect: the absence of an atom from a site in a crystal lattice (Fig. 6.1).

Schottky transition: a gradual transition in which the specific heat rises to a broad maximum around the transition temperature (Fig. 1.11).

scintillation counter: a device using luminescent crystals to count ionizing particles or radiation.

screw dislocation: a one-dimensional defect of crystals (Fig. 6.3).

secondary electron: an electron emitted following bombardment with primary electrons.

s-electrons: electrons with a secondary quantum number, $l=0$, whose charge density pattern has spherical symmetry.

self-diffusion: the exchange of atoms within a solid, which can only be detected using radioactive atoms.

semiconductor: a solid, usually opaque, with an electrical resistivity between 100 and 10^9 ohm cm.

sharp transition: see first order transition.

simple ion: a monatomic ion.

smectic: containing flat molecules oriented in layers.

solid: a state of matter in which the mean positions of the constituent atoms or molecules are fixed by their energy of interaction, so that both shape and volume are constant.

solubility: the amount of one substance which will dissolve in another.

solution: a homogeneous mixture of two substances.

solvation: the addition of solvent molecules to a dissolved molecule or ion.

solvent: a liquid used to dissolve substances.

sonoluminescence: luminescence excited by sound waves.

specific heat: the energy needed to raise 1 g of substance through 1°K at 1 atmosphere, divided by the energy needed to raise 1 g of water from 288° to 289°K: otherwise $T(\partial S/\partial T)_p$, where S is the entropy and T the temperature.

spectrum: the set of all transitions between energy levels of a system.

spin: a property of fundamental particles related to their magnetic moments.

stable: not decomposed by moderate or intense heat *in vacuo*.

stoicheiometric: containing atoms of two or more kinds in numbers whose ratios are extactly equal to ratios of small integers.

stress: the pressure on a solid.

sublime: to vaporize without melting.

superconduction: conduction of electricity with no measurable resistance.

supercool: to cool below a transition temperature without the transition occurring.

susceptibility (magnetic): the ratio of the magnetic field strength in a material to the magnetic field strength if the material is replaced by a vacuum.

temperature, T: a measure of the average energy of the atoms or molecules in a system at equilibrium.

tetrahedron: a regular figure with four apices and four faces (Fig. 1.13).

thermal conductivity: the rate of transfer of heat by conduction across unit length of material of unit cross-sectional area for a 1° difference in temperature.

thermal energy: the mean thermal energy of an atom or molecule at any temperature T is $1 \cdot 5kT$, where k is Boltzmann's constant.

thermal expansion coefficient: the ratio of the change in volume per degree temperature rise to the volume at 273°K: or $V^{-1}(\partial V/\partial T)_p$, where V is the volume.

thermal neutron: a neutron with thermal energy, e.g., 0·025 eV at 288°K.

thermistor: a device based on the variation of electrical conductivity of semiconductors with temperature, used to measure temperatures (see page 107).

thermodynamics: the study of the transformations of energy, heat, and work, with two important laws for closed systems:

  1. Energy is conserved.
  2. Entropy tends to a maximum value.

thermoelectric emission: emission of electrons on heating (=thermionic effect).

third law of thermodynamics: the entropy of a pure substance at absolute zero is zero.

transition temperature: the temperature at which one form of a substance changes into another.

triboluminescence: luminescence excited by pressure.

trigonal bipyramid: a geometrical figure with five apices (see Fig. 4.6).

trivalent: with a valency of three.

ultra-violet: electromagnetic radiation with energy between 3·5 and 25 eV.

unit crystal cell: the smallest parallelopiped from which a crystal may be built up by indefinite replication in three dimensions.

valency: of an element, is the number of atoms of H, Cl, or F with which one atom of that element will combine to form a stable compound: an element may have more than one valency.

valency electrons: the outer electrons of an atom that are used for bonding.

Van der Waals forces: a general term for forces between atoms and molecules which are neither covalent, ionic, nor metallic (see chapter 2).

velocity of light: $= 2 \cdot 99776 \times 10^{10}$ cm sec^{-1} *in vacuo.*

vibration spectrum: a spectrum arising from the vibrational energy levels of molecules; such spectra occur in the infra-red region.

visible region: electromagnetic radiation with energy between 1·7 and 3·5 eV.

volatile: easily vaporized.

volt, V: a unit of potential difference between two points, which need 10^7 ergs to transfer 1 coulomb from one to the other.

whiskers: small, perfect crystals of great mechanical strength.

work function: the minimum energy needed to expel an electron from a solid.

X-radiation: electromagnetic radiation with energy between 25 and 10^5 eV.

Energy interconversion chart

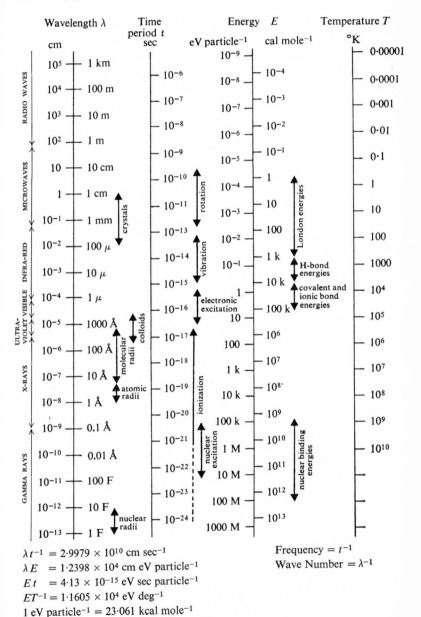

$\lambda t^{-1} = 2 \cdot 9979 \times 10^{10}$ cm sec^{-1}

$\lambda E = 1 \cdot 2398 \times 10^4$ cm eV particle^{-1}

$E t = 4 \cdot 13 \times 10^{-15}$ eV sec particle^{-1}

$ET^{-1} = 1 \cdot 1605 \times 10^4$ eV deg^{-1}

1 eV particle^{-1} = 23·061 kcal mole^{-1}

Frequency = t^{-1}

Wave Number = λ^{-1}

Index

Printed by Spottiswoode, Ballantyne & Co. Ltd., London and Colchester